Exploring Science 3

Mark Levesley
Sandra Baggley
Julian Clarke
Steve Gray
Penny Johnson

Longman

Edinburgh Gate
Harlow, Essex

Contents

Physics

What are microbes?

Living things are called **organisms**. Some organisms are very small (often made of only one cell) and we need microscopes to see them. Organisms like this are called **micro-organisms**, or **microbes** for short.

The seven life processes
Movement (move all or parts of themselves)
Reproduction (make more living things like themselves)
Sensitivity (sense and react to things around them)
Growth (increase in cell size and/or number)
Respiration (use a chemical reaction to release energy from food)
Excretion (get rid of waste materials that they make)
Nutrition (need various substances to help them respire and grow)

All organisms must do all these things.

 1 How many cells do many micro-organisms have?

Viruses are the smallest type of microbe. They are very difficult to see even with the most powerful microscope. The largest ones are only about 0.000 000 3 mm big! Many scientists do not think that they are organisms at all because they cannot live without being inside another cell.

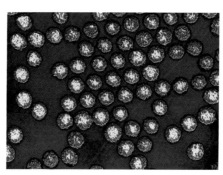

Viruses at a magnification of ×220 000.

 2 Why are viruses so difficult to see?

3 List two things that organisms do which viruses do not do for themselves.

A bacterium at a magnification of ×90 000.

Yeast cells at magnification of ×1380

Bacteria are much bigger than viruses and are definitely living things. The singular of bacteria is **bacterium**.

Another group of organisms are **fungi** (the singular is **fungus**). Some fungi, like mushrooms, are made of many cells. Others, like **yeasts**, are microbes and made of one cell. Yeasts are usually bigger than bacteria.

 When yeast respire they use up a sugar (like glucose) and produce carbon dioxide. How might you find out the best conditions for yeast to respire?

water   glucose   yeast culture

 4 a) Which are easier to see under a microscope, viruses or bacteria?

b) Explain your answer.

5 Name one sort of fungus that is a microbe.

You should know...

● **Viruses, bacteria and some fungi are microbes.**

Microbe structure

What are the major differences between microbes?

Organisms can be **classified** into one of five **kingdoms** by what their cells look like.

 1 Which kingdoms contain organisms that can make their own food?

Cell part	Kingdom				
	Bacteria	Protoctists	Fungi	Plants	Animals
Nucleus	Absent	Present	Present	Present	Present
Cell wall	Soft cell wall made of glycoprotein	Different types in different species	Mainly made of chitin	Mainly made of cellulose	Absent
Chloroplasts	Absent	Found in some species	Absent	Present	Absent

Viruses are not really living and so do not have a kingdom. They are made of a **protein coat** which contains a **strand of genes**. The genes contain the instructions for making new viruses. When a virus gets into a cell, the virus genes cause the cell to make new copies of the virus. This is known as **replication**.

Bacteria are single cells which do not contain a nucleus. Their genes are found on a circular **chromosome**. On the outside of a bacterium is a soft cell wall. Some bacteria have 'tails' (called **flagellae**) which help them move.

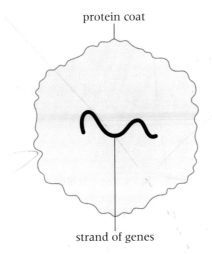

protein coat

strand of genes

A virus is very simple.

 2 What is a virus made up of?

3 a) What is virus replication?
   b) Why do you think it is not called 'reproduction'?

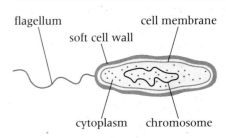

flagellum   cell membrane
soft cell wall   cytoplasm   chromosome

Bacteria are living cells.

 4 a) List one thing that an animal cell has but a bacterium cell does not.
   b) List two things that both animal cells and bacterium cells have.

Like all fungi, yeast have a nucleus which contains chromosomes. They also have vacuoles to store substances in.

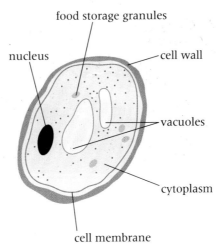

food storage granules
nucleus
cell wall
vacuoles
cytoplasm
cell membrane

Yeast cells are more complex than bacterium cells.

 5 List two differences between bacterium cells and yeast cells.

6 Algae (singular = alga) are a type of protoctist. Find and draw a diagram showing an alga cell. Label your drawing and write down the name of the alga. Write down where you found out the information.

How are microbes used?

Many microbes are useful. Some bacteria and fungi are used to make foods and drinks.

Some types of yeast are very important and are used in baking and brewing.

1 List three foods or drinks that are made with the help of yeast.

made with the help of fungi

made with the help of bacteria

made with the help of fungi and bacteria

Baking

Bread dough contains flour, water, sugar and yeast. The sugar allows the yeast to grow, respire and reproduce.

The dough is stretched and folded (kneaded) to trap air in it so that the yeast have enough oxygen for **aerobic respiration**.

2 Why is bread kneaded?

3 What is the word equation for aerobic respiration?

glucose + oxygen ⟶ carbon dioxide + water (+ energy)
(a sugar)

Aerobic respiration produces carbon dioxide. The bubbles of this gas make the dough rise.

The dough is then baked in an oven.

P How could you find out the best conditions for getting bread to rise the furthest?

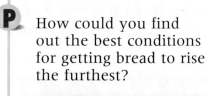

water

Brewing

Beer and wine are also made using yeast. However, this time the aim is to keep air out of the mixture. If there is no oxygen, yeast use **anaerobic respiration** instead, which produces **ethanol** (alcohol). When yeast respire anaerobically it is known as **fermentation**. If the yeast respire on sugars found in barley grains, beer is made. Grapes are used to make wine.

 Usually when making wine, the carbon dioxide escapes. When champagne is made, they make sure that the carbon dioxide stays in the wine to give it its fizz.

glucose ⟶ **carbon dioxide + ethanol (+ energy)**
(a sugar)

4 a) What is anaerobic respiration?
   b) What is it called when yeast respire anaerobically?

Yeast reproduce by **budding**. A new cell grows out of a 'parent' cell. The new cell grows and then it too can produce a 'bud cell'.

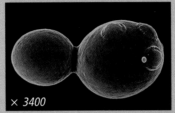

× 3400

Given the right conditions (warmth, moisture and plenty of sugar), microbes like yeast will grow and reproduce very quickly. Starting off with a few yeast cells, you can soon end up with many millions. However, the **population** of yeast cells will not keep growing forever. Eventually the sugar will run out and the population will stop growing. Something that slows down or stops a population growing is known as a **limiting factor**.

Only a few yeast cells and so the population increases slowly.

Many more yeast cells and so the population grows very quickly.

As the glucose starts to run out (becomes a limiting factor) the growth of the population slows down, and the population soon stops growing.

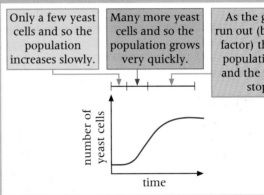

number of yeast cells

time

 5 What is a 'population'?

6 Some yeast cells are added to a beaker of glucose solution. The number of yeast cells is found to increase for eight hours and then it stops increasing.
   a) Why did the number of cells increase?
   b) Why did the number of cells stop increasing?

7 Some bread dough is made so that it contains hardly any air. The dough still rises. What process do you think happens to allow the bread to rise?

8 Draw a series of diagrams to show how one yeast cell will become three.

9 Choose one of the *foods* from the first picture on this spread and find out how bacteria or fungi are used to help make it.

You should know...

● Microbes can be used to help make foods.

● Yeast is used in baking and brewing.

● Anaerobic respiration is respiration that does not need oxygen.

● The growth of a population is controlled by limiting factors (eg amount of food available).

What diseases are caused by microbes and how are they spread?

Microbes are all around us. Most are harmless, but some have unpleasant effects, like making food go bad or milk sour. Some cause **diseases**.

You can usually tell that you have a disease by the effects it has on your body. These effects are known as the **symptoms** of the disease.

1 'Colds' are a common disease caused by viruses. Write down two symptoms of a cold.

This table shows you some diseases and their symptoms.

Diseases caused by viruses	
Flu (short for influenza)	High temperature (**fever**), sore throat, aches
Measles	Fever, red eyes, flat red spots on face and chest (more on the face)
Chicken pox	Fever, raised red spots with yellow tops found on face and chest (more on chest)
Diseases caused by bacteria	
Food poisoning	Vomiting, stomach pain, diarrhoea
Impetigo	Blisters cover the face and chest which leave yellow scabs
Syphilis	A pale red rash covers the whole body
Tuberculosis (TB)	Fever, tiredness, coughing up blood
Diseases caused by fungi	
Athlete's foot	Skin between the toes is red, itchy and peeling
Thrush (caused by yeast)	White patches in the mouth or vagina

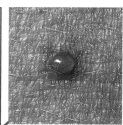
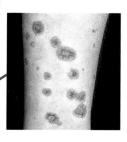
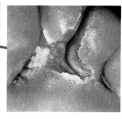

Diseases that can be spread from person to person (or from animal to person) are called **infectious** diseases. These diseases are spread in many different ways.

There are bacteria all over your body and you can never get rid of them! Bacteria in the armpits cause body odour (BO). Deodorants help to hide body odour.

2 Name one disease caused by:
a) a fungus   b) a virus
c) a bacterium.

3 a) What are the symptoms of food poisoning?
b) Find out the name of one bacterium that can cause food poisoning.

4 Many diseases cause a 'fever'. What is a fever?

Air

When someone coughs or sneezes, a spray of tiny watery droplets enters the air. These droplets may contain microbes. If someone else breathes in the droplets they may become **infected** by the microbes and get a disease. Colds, flu, chicken pox, measles and TB are all spread in this way.

Touch

Some diseases are passed on by touching an infected person (eg impetigo). Athlete's foot can be spread by touch or indirectly, by treading barefoot on a wet floor where an infected person has recently trodden.

Water

Cholera is a disease caused by a bacterium that is found in dirty water.

Food

Food poisoning is caused by bacteria found in food. The bacteria are usually killed by cooking.

Animals

Some microbes are carried by animals. For example, mosquitoes carry the microbes that cause malaria and yellow fever.

Sex

Some diseases are passed on when people have sex. Syphilis is an example.

Special photography can show up the droplets in a sneeze. The droplets in a sneeze may come out of your nose at 100 km/h.

5 What is an infectious disease?

6 Name a disease spread through the air, caused by:
a) a virus b) a bacterium.

7 Name a disease spread by touch, caused by:
a) a bacterium b) a fungus.

Cholera is often found in regions hit by a natural disaster when sewage gets into clean water supplies. The photograph shows people in Sahapur, West Bengal just after floods in September 2000.

8 a) What sort of microbe is cholera caused by?
b) Why do you think cholera occurs in areas hit by disasters?

9 When a doctor works out what is wrong with someone, he or she is said to make a **diagnosis**. Imagine you are a doctor and three people come to see you. Their photos are shown below.
a) What diagnosis would you make for each of your patients, A, B and C?
b) Suggest how each person may have got their disease.

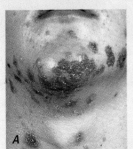
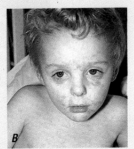
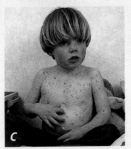

A   B   C

You should know...

- **The name of a disease caused by each of the different sorts of microbes.**
- **The different ways diseases can be spread.**

How did John Snow work out how cholera was spread?

Cholera is an infectious disease which causes very bad diarrhoea and vomiting. In the nineteenth century, cholera killed many people.

Dr. John Snow made careful **observations** of where and how infected people lived. He found that people with the disease often had a different water supply from their neighbours who remained healthy. He came up with a **theory** that cholera was spread in the water. A theory is a scientific idea that can be tested. He thought that something inside infected people came out in their faeces and if the faeces got into the water, other people caught the disease.

In 1854 nearly 500 people died in ten days in an area around Broad Street in London. In those days, people in this area got water from pumps in the streets. Snow marked the deaths on a map and also drew in the positions of the pumps.

He **predicted** that if people stopped using the Broad Street pump, they would stop getting cholera. He got the pump handle removed, and soon afterwards, people did stop getting cholera. This provided more **evidence** that his theory was right.

People started to believe Snow's theory, but it wasn't until 1883 that the bacterium that causes cholera was found.

1 Why did Snow think that cholera was spread by water?

2 William Farr had a theory that cholera was caused by 'bad air'. Why do you think Snow didn't believe this theory?

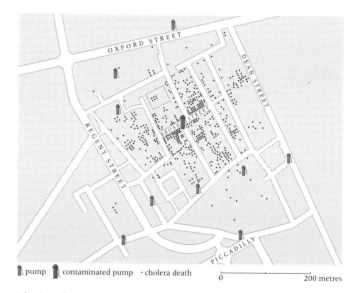

pump contaminated pump · cholera death   0   200 metres

John Snow's map. Each spot represents a death.

A replica of the pump now outside the John Snow pub in Broadwick Street (which used to be called Broad Street). Notice that it has no handle.

3 a) What is a theory?
   b) What evidence supported Snow's theory? Use the map to help you.

4 a) What sort of microbe causes cholera?
   b) What are the symptoms of cholera?

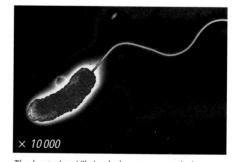

× 10 000

The bacterium Vibrio cholerae *causes cholera.*

You should know...
● **What a theory is.**

How do we stop the spread of diseases?

In the middle of the nineteenth century, cities smelled disgusting. Sewage was often stored in cellars (cesspits) under houses or flowed into the streets where it collected in small ditches in the road. The sewage often leaked into the water supply.

Diseases were very common; poor workmen in London often died before reaching the age of 20! After it was discovered that the sewage in drinking water caused diseases, sewer tunnels were built and water was used to wash the sewage away. This greatly reduced the number of people with diseases.

Proper sewage disposal was the most important development in stopping people dying from diseases. Today, we also try to kill microbes or stop them growing.

! A sewer tunnel designed in 1858 by Isambard Kingdom Brunel went under the Thames. Queen Victoria liked it so much that she asked for a railway to be put in it. It never became a sewer and today it is part of the Bakerloo Underground line!

Method	Used to ...	Prevents the spread of ...
Pasteurisation	Pasteurise milk (heated up to 70 °C for about 15 seconds which kills harmful bacteria)	Tuberculosis
Disinfectants	Kill bacteria in toilets and around buildings	Stomach upsets, Legionnaire's disease
Soaps and **antiseptics** (found in toothpaste and antiperspirants)	Kill bacteria on our bodies	Skin diseases, stomach upsets
Adding chlorine to drinking water supplies	Kill harmful bacteria in the water	Cholera, typhoid, stomach upsets
Salting, canning, pickling in vinegar	Kill bacteria and fungi in food	Stomach upsets
Drying, freezing, refrigeration	Stop or slow down the growth of bacteria and fungi in food	Stomach upsets
Cooking foods well	Kill off bacteria	Food poisoning

P Bacteria can be grown on a special jelly called agar. How could you find out if washing with soap helps to remove bacteria? Or is plain water just as good?

? 1 Why do you think building sewers reduced the number of people with diseases?

2 Make a list of all the ways in which bacteria have been stopped from getting to you so far today.

3 a) What is pasteurisation?
b) Why do you think pasteurisation has helped to make tuberculosis a much less common disease?

You should know...
● **Methods of killing bacteria.**

11

How does your body protect you against diseases?

Your body has ways of killing microbes and stopping them getting inside you. These are your **natural defences**.

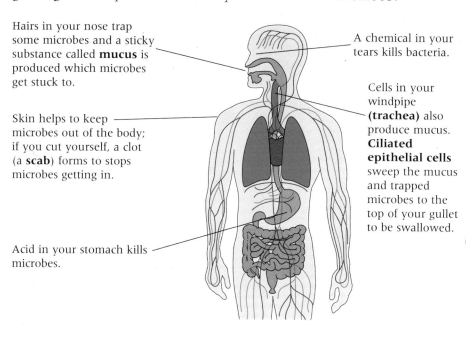

Hairs in your nose trap some microbes and a sticky substance called **mucus** is produced which microbes get stuck to.

Skin helps to keep microbes out of the body; if you cut yourself, a clot (a **scab**) forms to stops microbes getting in.

Acid in your stomach kills microbes.

A chemical in your tears kills bacteria.

Cells in your windpipe **(trachea)** also produce mucus. **Ciliated epithelial cells** sweep the mucus and trapped microbes to the top of your gullet to be swallowed.

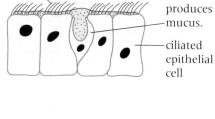

cilia

This cell produces mucus.

ciliated epithelial cell

White blood cells destroy microbes. Some of them surround (**engulf**) microbes.

Other white blood cells make **antibodies**. These stick to microbes, making it easier for them to be engulfed. Antibodies can also make the microbes stick together or burst open. However, antibodies have to be specially made to attach to each different sort of microbe and this takes time.

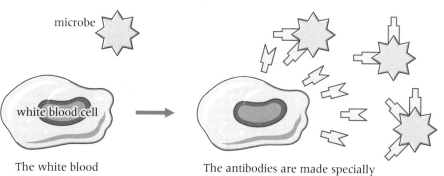

microbe

white blood cell

The white blood cell finds a microbe and starts to make antibodies.

The antibodies are made specially to fit onto the outside of the microbe. Each type of microbe has a different surface and so needs a different type of antibody.

? 1 Why is it important for a scab to form quickly?

2 a) What is mucus?
   b) What does it do?
   c) Name two places where it is produced.

3 a) List three things antibodies can do to microbes.
   b) Why does it take time for antibodies to be produced?

4 Antibodies are said to be 'specific' for a certain microbe. What do you think this means?

You should know...
● **How natural defences protect you from microbes.**
● **How white blood cells destroy microbes.**

How does immunisation work?

If you get **infected** with microbes, they reproduce. It takes time for your body to make antibodies and so you get the disease until there are enough antibodies in your blood to destroy all the microbes.

When you have recovered from a disease, some antibodies stay in your blood, often forever. This means that your body is ready for that particular microbe if it infects you again. You will not get that disease again and you are said to be **immune**.

Injections which contain a **vaccine** protect us from diseases. This is called **immunisation** and it makes the body produce antibodies against a microbe.

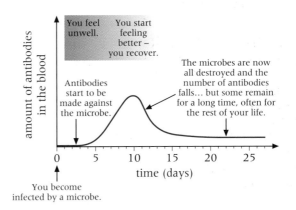

You feel unwell.

You start feeling better – you recover.

The microbes are now all destroyed and the number of antibodies falls... but some remain for a long time, often for the rest of your life.

Antibodies start to be made against the microbe.

amount of antibodies in the blood

time (days)

You become infected by a microbe.

> **1** What does it mean if someone is immune to a disease?

Age of person	Vaccine given
2–4 months	Diphtheria, whooping cough, polio, tetanus, bacterial meningitis
1–2 years	Measles, mumps, rubella
3–5 years	Diphtheria, tetanus, polio
10–14 years (girls only)	Rubella
13 years	Tuberculosis
16–19 years	Tetanus, polio
Adults	Tetanus every 5–10 years

Normal ages for immunisations in the UK. You need some immunisations more than once to make sure that your body builds up high enough levels of antibodies. The extra injections are called 'boosters'.

A vaccine contains the microbes that normally cause a disease but which have been treated to stop them doing this. Your body produces antibodies against the treated microbes. Many of these stay in your blood ready to help quickly destroy the real microbes if you ever become infected by them. You become immune to the disease.

> **2** Sketch a graph to show the changes in the number of antibodies after an immunisation.
>
> **3** Name two immunisations that require 'boosters' to be given.
>
> **4** Chicken pox and measles are caused by viruses.
> a) Explain why you can only get chicken pox once.
> b) If you have had chicken pox, will it stop you from getting measles? Explain your answer.
> c) How can you make sure you never get measles?

Edward Jenner (1749–1823) invented vaccines. He gave people a mild disease called cowpox to stop them getting smallpox (a very nasty disease). Thanks to immunisation smallpox no longer exists. The last case was in Africa in 1978.

The skin of a child with smallpox.

You should know...
- **Why immunisations are given.**

How do antibiotics work?

Vaccines cannot be made for every disease but **medicines** can help treat and cure many diseases.

Antibiotics are medicines that harm bacteria. They were discovered by Alexander Fleming in 1928 when he looked at some bacteria growing on agar jelly. A mould had also grown on the agar, and Fleming observed that the bacteria were not growing near the mould.

Fleming came up with a theory that the mould produced a chemical which harmed the bacteria. He was right, and along with two other scientists (Howard Florey and Ernst Chain), made the first antibiotic – penicillin. There are now many different antibiotics, and different ones harm different bacteria. Bacteria that are not harmed by an antibiotic are said to be **resistant** to it.

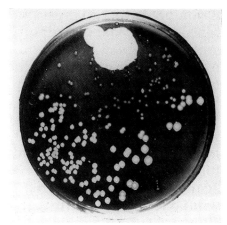

One of Fleming's Petri dishes. The mould is at the top. Notice that only clumps of bacteria growing far away from the mould grow well.

P Bacteria can be grown in Petri dishes containing agar. Antibiotics can be tested by soaking disks of paper in antibiotics and putting the disks on the agar. How would you test three antibiotics against a bacterium called *E. coli*? How would you tell which was the best antibiotic?

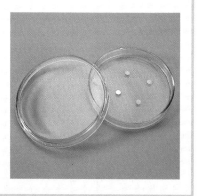

1 What are antibiotics?

2 a) What theory did Fleming come up with?
   b) What evidence supported this theory?

3 What does it mean if a bacterium is resistant to an antibiotic?

4 Why can't colds be cured by antibiotics?

5 What does aspirin do?

6 Why do you think Fleming named his antibiotic Penicillin?

The skins of toads produce their own antibiotics.

Antibiotics don't work against viruses. When a disease is caused by a virus you can usually only ease the symptoms. If you have a fever, medicines like aspirin and paracetamol can reduce your temperature and help stop you aching.

Other medicines can treat problems not caused by microbes, like cancer, indigestion and travel sickness.

You should know...
● **What antibiotics are used for.**

HIV and AIDS

What is AIDS and how is it spread?

AIDS stands for **A**cquired **I**mmune **D**eficiency **S**yndrome and is caused by the **H**uman **I**mmunodeficiency **V**irus (**HIV**).

AIDS is a killer disease with no cure and no vaccine. Around the world there are 16 000 new infections every day. People in Africa are particularly badly affected.

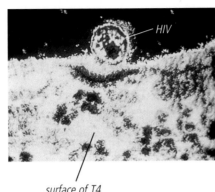

surface of T4 lymphocyte

People with the virus are **HIV positive**. HIV infects white blood cells called **T4 lymphocytes**, which are vital for destroying microbes in the body. The virus gets into the cells, and DNA from it is inserted into the cell's DNA.

The HIV DNA causes the lymphocytes to **replicate** (make new copies of) the virus. These burst out of the cell and destroy it.

Over many years the number of HIV viruses increases. Eventually, so many T4 lymphocytes are destroyed that the person gets many other diseases, and is said to have AIDS. It is these other diseases that kill the person.

HIV is spread through sex and by drug addicts sharing needles. HIV-positive pregnant mothers can also pass it on to their unborn babies. It cannot be passed on by coming into normal contact with an HIV-positive person. Using a condom during sex stops the virus from passing from person to person.

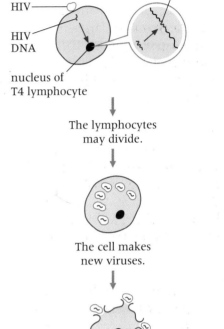

The lymphocytes may divide.

The cell makes new viruses.

The viruses burst out of the cell.

1 Explain how millions of T4 lymphocytes can get infected with the virus if only one gets into the body.

2 Why might a person with AIDS die from a disease caused by a bacterium?

3 a) How is HIV spread?
   b) How can its spread be stopped?

4 Why do you think HIV has the name it does?

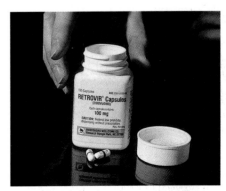

There are anti-HIV medicines, like zidovudine. These stop the virus from infecting too many new cells but they are not a cure.

What is photosynthesis?

All the trees in this forest grew from tiny seeds and, over the years, they have grown bigger and taller. Unlike most animals, plants continue to grow throughout their lives.

People used to the think that plants got all the things they needed to grow from the soil. However, if this were true, then all the soil in a forest would soon be used up and this obviously does not happen!

Even very large trees grow from tiny seeds. The most massive organism on Earth is thought to be this sequoia tree (nick-named 'General Sherman').

Jean-Baptiste van Helmont (1579–1644).

A Belgian scientist called Jean-Baptiste van Helmont did an experiment to show that plants do not get everything they need from the soil. He took a pot of dry soil and measured its mass. He planted a small willow tree with a mass of 2.27 kg in it and watered it regularly for five years. He then dried out the soil and measured the masses of the pot of dry soil and the tree again. He found that the mass of the soil was only 60 g less but the tree now had a mass of nearly 77 kg.

1 a) Why did van Helmont need to water his willow tree?
   b) Some people suggested that all the extra mass of van Helmont's tree came from the water that he added. Do you think this was a sensible suggestion? Explain your answer.

Today we know that plants need carbon dioxide from the air as well as water from the soil to make their own food. The process that they use to make their food is called **photosynthesis**. Carbon dioxide and water are the **raw materials** (**reactants**) for photosynthesis. The food made is a sugar. There are many different sorts of sugars but the one made in photosynthesis is called **glucose**. Oxygen is also made in photosynthesis.

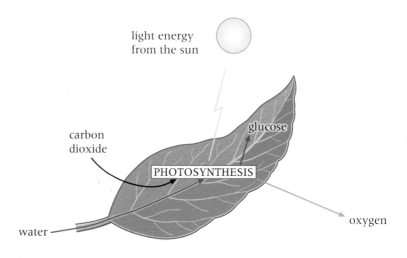

light energy from the sun

carbon dioxide

glucose

PHOTOSYNTHESIS

water

oxygen

Photosynthesis mainly occurs in leaves.

Light energy is needed to make photosynthesis happen and so it only occurs when it is light. During photosynthesis, the light energy is changed into chemical energy which is stored in the glucose. Since photosynthesis is a chemical reaction we can write it down as a **word equation**.

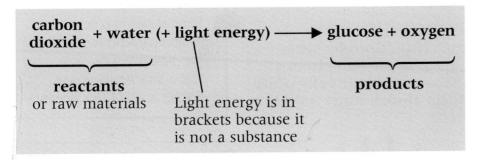

carbon dioxide + **water (+ light energy)** ⟶ **glucose + oxygen**

reactants
or raw materials

Light energy is in brackets because it is not a substance

products

Bubbles of oxygen can often be seen coming from Canadian pondweed. The more bubbles, the faster photosynthesis is happening. How would you find out what factors affect the amount (rate) of photosynthesis?
• You will only need to use some of this apparatus!
• Look at the word equation to help you choose a factor to change.
• Sodium hydrogen carbonate can be added to water to increase the amount of carbon dioxide in it.

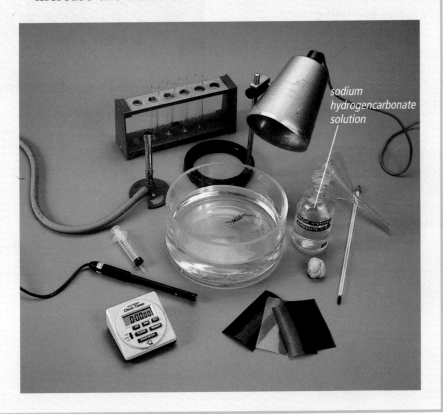

sodium hydrogencarbonate solution

2 Copy and complete the sentences using words from this list:

carbon dioxide   cellulose chlorophyll   glucose light   oxygen   water

a) The raw materials for photosynthesis are _____ and _____ _____.

b) The sugar made by photosynthesis is _____.

c) Photosynthesis needs _____ energy.

3 Why do plants in a field only photosynthesise during the day?

4 Why is light energy not a reactant (raw material)?

5 What form of energy is light energy turned into in a plant?

You should know...
● **Plants use photosynthesis to make their own food.**
● **The word equation for photosynthesis.**

How do plants get the things they need for photosynthesis?

Getting water

The water for photosynthesis is taken out of the soil by the roots. Roots are **adapted** to their job (**function**) by being branched and spread out, helping them to get water from a large volume of the soil. They also have **root hair cells** which have a large surface area to help them **absorb** water quickly.

 Some plants grow huge numbers of roots very quickly. Rye grass plants can grow roots with a total length of over 600 km in about four months.

Roots get a lot of water out of the soil by being branched and spread out.

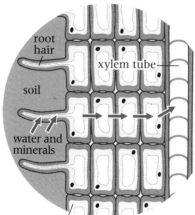

Many **root hair cells** grouped together form root hair tissue.

1 a) What problem might a plant have if its roots were not spread out?
 b) What do root hair cells do?
 c) How are they adapted to their function?

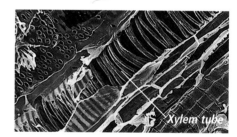

Xylem tube

The water goes through the root hair cells and other cells in the root until it reaches **xylem tubes**. These are long hollow tubes made out of dead xylem cells which carry water up to the leaves.

Water is also needed by plants to keep their leaves cool and to fill up their cells to help them grow and to keep them firm. If there is too little water, the cells start to sag and the plant droops – it **wilts**. The water absorbed from the soil also contains dissolved **mineral salts** which a plant needs to stay healthy.

2 a) Water goes from the roots to the leaves. Explain how.
 b) The cells that carry the water are adapted to their function. Explain how.

3 Look at the photograph of the celery stem in dye.
 a) Where in the plant will the dye travel to. Suggest why.
 b) What would you see if the water was dyed red?

4 a) Give two examples of tissues from this page.
 b) Give two examples of organs from this page.

5 List three reasons why plants need water.

Getting carbon dioxide

There are small holes in a leaf called **stomata** (singular = stoma). These are opened and closed by **guard cells**. When the stomata are open, usually when there is light, carbon dioxide enters the leaf by **diffusion**. Leaves are thin so that the carbon dioxide does not have to go very far into a leaf before getting to cells that need it.

 P How would you examine some xylem tubes in detail?

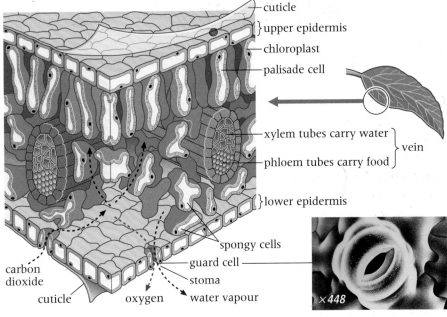

cuticle
}upper epidermis
chloroplast
palisade cell
xylem tubes carry water } vein
phloem tubes carry food }
}lower epidermis
spongy cells
carbon dioxide
guard cell
cuticle
stoma
oxygen
water vapour

The inside of a leaf.

×448

A stoma.

Getting light

Photosynthesis happens in the **chloroplasts**. These contain a green substance called **chlorophyll** which absorbs the light energy from the Sun to make photosynthesis happen. Most photosynthesis happens in the **palisade cells**. They are adapted to their function by containing a lot of chloroplasts.

Plants growing in shady areas often have very big leaves.

The more light a plant can get, the more photosynthesis will happen. Therefore, the leaves of plants growing in shady places tend to be very big (they have a large surface area) so that they can absorb as much of the light as possible.

? 6 Choose one word from this spread which best fits each of these descriptions.
   a) Cells which open and close stomata.
   b) The movement of particles from an area where there are many of them to an area where there are few of them.

7 A gas diffuses out of the leaf and into the air. What is this gas?

? 8 a) What coloured substance, produced by a plant, is needed for photosynthesis?
   b) What does this substance do?
   c) In which cells do you think most photosynthesis happens? Explain your answer.

9 Why are leaves thin?

10 Why do you think plants that grow beneath trees in forests make good houseplants?

You should know...
- How water and carbon dioxide get to the leaves of a plant.
- How leaves are adapted for photosynthesis.
- How roots are adapted to their functions.
- Why water is needed by plants.

How do plants get the energy they need to grow?

Every living cell in a plant needs a supply of glucose to provide energy. Energy is needed to help the plant grow and to make new substances. The chemical energy stored in glucose is released by **aerobic respiration** – another chemical reaction:

glucose + oxygen ⟶ carbon dioxide + water (+ energy)

The word equation for aerobic respiration. It is called 'aerobic' because it needs oxygen from the air.

Photosynthesis can only happen when there is light, but respiration happens *all* the time. During the day, a plant produces more oxygen from photosynthesis than it needs for respiration and so oxygen is given off by the leaves through the stomata. At night, only respiration is happening and so the plant uses up oxygen.

> **2** Look at the graph. It shows the concentrations of oxygen and carbon dioxide in the water around a pondweed plant over the course of 24 hours.
>
> a) Which letter (A–D) do you think represents 23:00 hrs?
> b) Which line do you think shows the oxygen concentration, X or Y?
> c) Explain why line X goes up between letters B and D.

Substances made by the plant can be carried around it dissolved in water. **Phloem tubes** carry dissolved substances to where they are needed all around the plant. These tubes are made from chains of living phloem cells.

Root cells take the glucose they need for respiration out of the phloem tubes. However, they also need oxygen which they have to get from the soil. If the soil gets flooded or waterlogged, the roots cannot get enough oxygen to respire and so the plants can die.

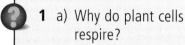

> **1** a) Why do plant cells respire?
> b) What are the two reactants in respiration?

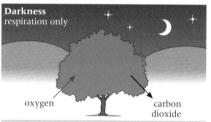

Darkness
respiration only

oxygen   carbon dioxide

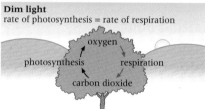

Dim light
rate of photosynthesis = rate of respiration

oxygen

photosynthesis   respiration

carbon dioxide

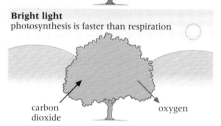

Bright light
photosynthesis is faster than respiration

carbon dioxide   oxygen

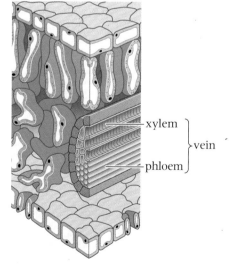

The inside of a leaf showing the vein.

xylem
vein
phloem

3 What are the tubes that carry dissolved sugars called?

4 Look at the photograph on the right. Why will these plants die?

These swamp cypresses are adapted to their habitat by having special roots that poke up above the water to get air.

breathing root

Most of the glucose made in the leaves by photosynthesis is turned into **starch**. Starch is an insoluble storage material. When needed, the starch is turned back into soluble sugars (like glucose) which are transported around the plant in the phloem tubes.

P This is a variegated leaf. The white parts contain no chlorophyll.

How could you show that chlorophyll is needed for photosynthesis to happen?
- When testing leaves you need to remove all the chlorophyll. This can be done by placing the leaves in hot ethanol for about 5 minutes.
- How would you do this experiment safely?

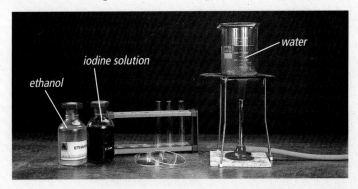

water

iodine solution

ethanol

5 What is the glucose from photosynthesis turned into?

6 a) Roots need a supply of glucose. Explain why.
b) How do they get the glucose?

7 Which area of a plant do you think would need more glucose – a new bud or an old part of a stem? Explain your answer.

8 What are the differences between xylem tubes and phloem tubes?

You should know...
- Every living cell in a plant respires all the time.
- The word equation for aerobic respiration.

Sugary food

How is glucose used by plants?

The glucose made in photosynthesis is used for:
- respiration
- making other substances that act as stores of energy (e.g. starch)
- making new materials for growth.

The new material that an organism makes is called its **biomass**. Therefore, the biomass is the mass of everything in an organism apart from water. To make new biomass and grow, a plant needs to make many new substances, like proteins. To make proteins, nitrogen-containing compounds called **nitrates** are needed. These are a type of **mineral salt** and are absorbed from the soil, along with water. Plants do not grow well without nitrates.

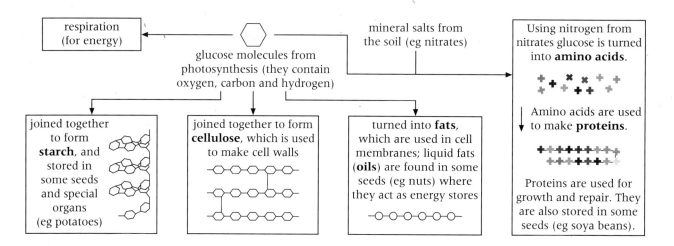

1 What is biomass?

2 In plants, what are the following used for:
   a) cellulose b) fats c) proteins?

3 a) Which of these substances might be used as an energy store in seeds? cellulose fats nitrates oxygen starch

   b) Why do you think seeds need a store of energy?
   c) What process do seeds use to release the energy?

4 Name four *elements* that plants need to grow.

5 a) Some elements are found in mineral salts. How does a plant get a supply of mineral salts?
   b) What are nitrates used for?
   c) Find out what potassium and phosphorus mineral salts are used for.

6 Look back at van Helmont's experiment on page 16. Explain why you think his soil lost a very small amount of mass.

Proteins, fats and carbohydrates (sugars and starch) are needed in our diets. How would you find out which parts of plants contained these food substances?

You should know...
- **Glucose is used to make cellulose, fats, proteins and starch.**

How can the growth of crop plants be speeded up?

Animals, including us, could not exist on earth without plants, since they provide oxygen and food. Humans also use plants for other things.

Sometimes, crops are grown in greenhouses where they can be given the best conditions for photosynthesis and growth.

1 Write down the name of one substance you would expect to find in each of these things. Use the information on the previous page to help you.

Plants photosynthesise best at about 30 °C (the **optimum temperature**). Sunlight heats up the greenhouse and the heat is trapped inside by the glass. Above 40 °C some of the enzymes involved in photosynthesis are damaged. Ventilation flaps can be opened to stop a greenhouse getting too hot.

Lights can be used to let the plants photosynthesise even when it's dark outside.

The more carbon dioxide, the more photosynthesis, and so carbon dioxide is sometimes pumped into greenhouses.

Too little water makes the plants wilt and photosynthesis slow down. Sprinkler systems can be used to provide the right amount of water.

2 a) Name three ways of increasing photosynthesis in a greenhouse.
   b) Why is increasing the amount of photosynthesis useful?

3 Explain why photosynthesis decreases at more than 40 °C.

4 Too much light can damage chloroplasts. What might be used in a greenhouse to stop this happening on a very sunny day?

5 In some greenhouses, paraffin is burnt in heaters. Paraffin is a hydrocarbon. Write down two ways in which using paraffin heaters increases the rate of photosynthesis.

How can plants be grown without soil?

Growing plants without soil is called **hydroponics**. The lettuces in the photograph are being grown in tubes through which water is flowing. The water contains mineral salts and lots of dissolved oxygen.

 1 The water in the tubes has to contain oxygen. Suggest why.

Another method is to grow the plants in growing medium and allow the water to continually drip onto the surface of the medium.

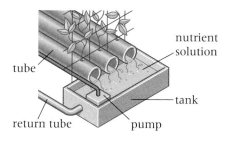

nutrient solution

tube

tank

return tube pump

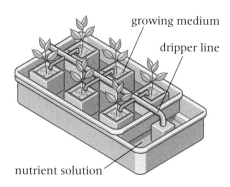

growing medium

dripper line

nutrient solution

 2 The water that is dripped onto plants does not need to have extra oxygen added to it. Why do you think this is?

The most important mineral salts are those containing nitrates, phosphates or potassium. Examples include potassium nitrate and potassium hydrogen phosphate. Nitrates are needed to make proteins and too little results in poor growth. Phosphates are needed to make cell membranes and for healthy root growth. Potassium is needed to help the enzymes in respiration and photosynthesis. A lack of potassium causes the leaves to turn yellow.

3 For each of these plants, write down:
   a) which mineral salt you think is lacking
   b) what this mineral salt is used for.

4 What do you think are the advantages and disadvantages of hydroponics?

5 A lot of mineral salts in the soil come from **humus** (rotting dead plants). Why do you think hydroponics is used in desert regions?

How are crops grown on farms?

The population of the world is increasing very quickly and so more food needs to be produced. There are many ways of getting as much food as possible from the land.

Forests are cut down to make new farmland and hedgerows are removed to create more space and allow big machines to get around more easily. Machines can help to plant and harvest crops faster than humans can.

New **varieties** of plants are bred which are better at producing food.

In 1951, one field of wheat in Canada covered an area of 350 km².

The wheat plants on the right are a variety that used to be grown in the 1950s. Those on the left are a variety grown today.

1 Why do you think farmers want to harvest their crops quickly?

2 a) What differences can be seen between the modern variety of wheat and the older one?
 b) Why do you think farmers now only plant the new variety of wheat?

Weeds **compete** with the crop plants for water, light and mineral salts, and so **herbicides** (**weedkillers**) are used. Modern herbicides destroy the weeds but not the crop.

Man-made fertilisers contain mineral salts to help plants grow. A natural fertiliser is manure, which is animal waste. Microbes and other small organisms, called **decomposers**, break down manure (and dead organisms) and so release mineral salts from them back into the soil.

Pests are organisms that damage crops (eg weeds, animals and fungi). Crops are often sprayed with an **insecticide** to kill insect pests.

The sugarbeet plants on the right have been sprayed with weedkiller. Those on the left have not.

The plants on the left have been given fertiliser. Those in the middle have not.

The first farm machine with moving parts was invented by a British farmer called Jethro Tull in 1701. It was used to plant seeds (a seed drill).

3 What is a pest?

4 Crops do not grow so well if there are weeds growing with them. Suggest why.

5 What do fertilisers contain that help plants to grow?

6 What is a decomposer?

You should know...

● **How crops are farmed to produce as much food as possible.**

What are the problems with farming?

Land is cleared to make space for crops and also to allow large machines to harvest crops more easily. Removing trees and hedgerows destroys the **habitats** of animals and so their numbers fall.

There are also other problems. The roots of the trees hold the soil together and without them the soil can be washed away by rain. This is an example of **soil erosion**.

 Turtle doves nest in large hedges. So many hedges have been destroyed that, since 1972, their population has gone down by 60%.

 *Between 1990 and 1993, 10 000 km of hedges were destroyed in the UK.*

1 The photograph shows an area of rain forest that was cleared a couple of years ago. Suggest why
a) it was cleared
b) there are very few plants there now.

Spraying insecticides kills all the insects in a field and often in the hedges too. Even helpful insects, which eat pests or pollinate plants, are killed. Some insecticides stay in the environment for a long time (they are **persistent**) and can poison other animals.

Selective herbicides only kill plants that have broad leaves, so a crop like wheat is not affected. But many plants in hedges have broad leaves and they are killed.

Fertilisers can be washed out of the soil and cause algae in lakes and rivers to grow very quickly. The overcrowded algae die. Bacteria feed on the dead algae and use up the oxygen in the water and so the fish also die.

2 This is a food web for a hedge next to a field of wheat. Explain as fully as you can what would happen if a farmer sprayed his crop with:
a) insecticide   b) selective herbicide.

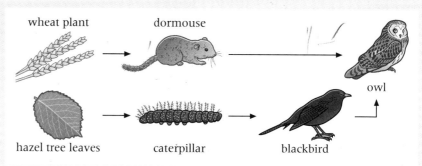

wheat plant — dormouse — owl

hazel tree leaves — caterpillar — blackbird

3 Prepare a table to show the advantages and disadvantages of: clearing land, using insecticides, using herbicides and using fertilisers.

You should know...
- **The harmful effects of land clearing and the use of chemicals in farming.**

What is the carbon cycle?

There are many processes that affect the amount of carbon dioxide in the atmosphere. The **carbon cycle** shows how these processes are linked.

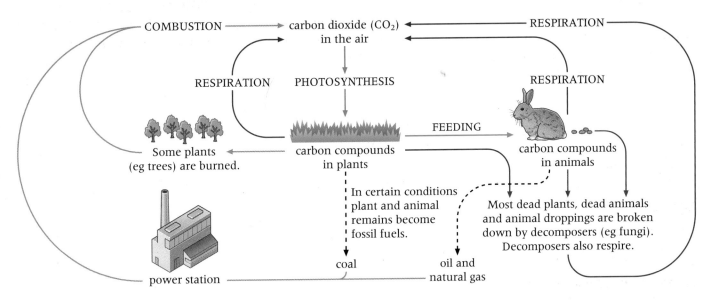

The amount of carbon dioxide in the atmosphere has been increasing for about the last 200 years. This is thought to be due to burning more fossil fuels, which produces carbon dioxide, and cutting down trees so that less carbon dioxide gets used up by photosynthesis.

Extra carbon dioxide traps heat in the atmosphere. This is called the **greenhouse effect**. It causes the Earth and its atmosphere to get hotter (**global warming**). Scientists are worried that global warming may change our weather and melt the ice at the North and South Poles.

Worldwide, 12 hectares (about the area of a village in the UK) of trees are cut down every minute.

1 a) List three ways that carbon dioxide is added to the atmosphere.
   b) Which of these ways has been increasing in the last 200 years?

2 This satellite map shows how much photosynthesis is happening around the world. The darker the green, the more photosynthesis.
   a) What do you think is in the areas that are *darkest* green?
   b) How might this map be changed in 100 years' time? Explain your answer.

3 a) Describe one way in which global warming is caused.
   b) What might happen if the ice at the North and South Poles melts?

Why must an astronaut be 'super fit' before going into space?

NASA has plans to launch a manned mission to Mars in 2018. The journey will take about six months. During this time the astronauts will live without gravity and without the normal days and nights that they are used to on Earth. This will cause problems for their bodies.

The mission to Mars will be launched from the International Space Station.

The dangers of space flight	
Problems caused by lack of gravity	Muscles get thinner and weaker Bones get thinner and weaker Circulatory system is less efficient Immune system does not work so well Dizziness, feeling sick (lasts for a few days)
Problems caused by no days and nights	Sleeping problems

Space life scientists work on these problems. They examine the **tissues** (like muscle and bone) of astronauts who have spent a lot of time in space.

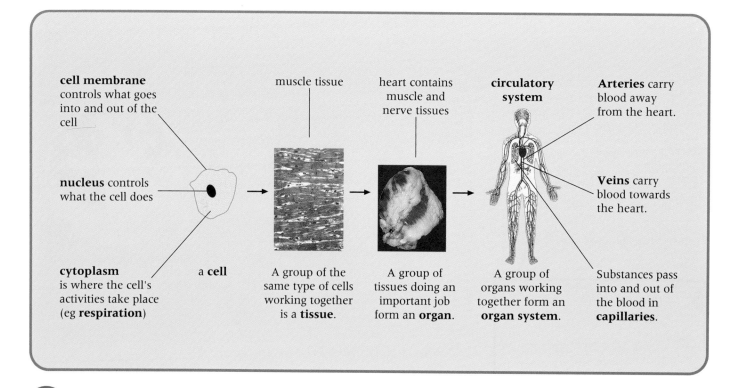

cell membrane controls what goes into and out of the cell

nucleus controls what the cell does

cytoplasm is where the cell's activities take place (eg **respiration**)

a **cell**

muscle tissue

A group of the same type of cells working together is a **tissue**.

heart contains muscle and nerve tissues

A group of tissues doing an important job form an **organ**.

circulatory system

A group of organs working together form an **organ system**.

Arteries carry blood away from the heart.

Veins carry blood towards the heart.

Substances pass into and out of the blood in **capillaries**.

The scientists have found that an astronaut loses about 2–3% of his or her muscle mass each month. This is because the muscles do not have gravity to work against. Muscles are vital for movement (eg the **triceps** and **biceps** in the arm). The heart muscles also get weaker in space, so blood carrying oxygen and food is not pumped so well.

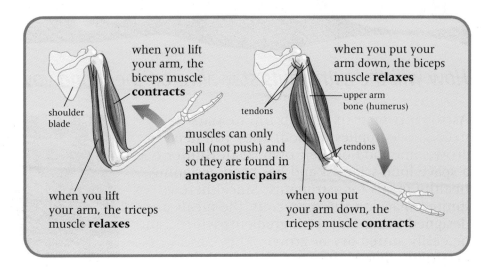

when you lift your arm, the biceps muscle **contracts**

shoulder blade

when you lift your arm, the triceps muscle **relaxes**

muscles can only pull (not push) and so they are found in **antagonistic pairs**

when you put your arm down, the biceps muscle **relaxes**

upper arm bone (humerus)

tendons

tendons

when you put your arm down, the triceps muscle **contracts**

The scientists have also found that an astronaut's bones get gradually thinner (by about 1–2% per month).

> **Bones are used for protection, movement (at joints) and support.**

For reasons that are not understood, the number of **white blood cells** in an astronaut goes down. They are less able to fight off diseases caused by **bacteria** and **viruses**.

Before astronauts go into space they must get very fit. They may also be given **immunisations** and **medicines** to stop them getting ill in the weeks leading up to launch. Once they are in space they need to exercise hard to stop their bodies wasting away.

This is Steven Hawley working out on board the Space Shuttle. Astronauts need to exercise for about four hours each day.

1 a) Draw a human cell and label its parts.
   b) Design a table to show what each part does.

2 a) Name two tissues found in the heart.
   b) What organ system is the heart a part of?
   c) What is the **heart beat rate**?
   d) How will this change when an astronaut exercises in space?
   e) Some astronauts get very out of breath when they exercise. Explain why they may get more out of breath in space than on Earth.

3 a) Name one antagonistic pair of muscles.
   b) Why are muscles found in antagonistic pairs?

4 What problems might be caused by an astronaut's bones getting thinner?

5 Why might an astronaut with a cold take longer to recover from it in space?

6 Humans need regular periods of light and dark to sleep properly. Do you think astronauts going to Mars will find it difficult to get to sleep? Explain your answer.

7 Estimate what percentage of these tissues would have been lost by an astronaut arriving on Mars:
   a) muscle tissue
   b) bone tissue.
   Explain how you worked out your answers.

How will the astronauts stay alive on their long voyage?

Astronauts on a six-month trip to Mars will need good supplies of food. They will need to grow some food of their own. Jean Hunter is a space food scientist and has been designing healthy meals for astronauts. Since there is limited space on the spacecraft, the meals are designed using only 15 ingredients which can be easily stored dry or grown. They have been carefully selected to give a **balanced diet**.

Dr. Jean Hunter

A sandwich designed by Dr. Jean Hunter containing the 15 ingredients available to astronauts.

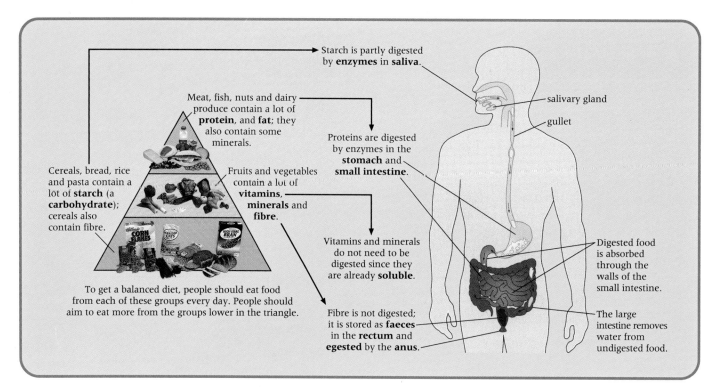

Starch is partly digested by **enzymes** in **saliva**.

Meat, fish, nuts and dairy produce contain a lot of **protein**, and **fat**; they also contain some minerals.

Cereals, bread, rice and pasta contain a lot of **starch** (a **carbohydrate**); cereals also contain fibre.

Fruits and vegetables contain a lot of **vitamins**, **minerals** and **fibre**.

Proteins are digested by enzymes in the **stomach** and **small intestine**.

Vitamins and minerals do not need to be digested since they are already **soluble**.

To get a balanced diet, people should eat food from each of these groups every day. People should aim to eat more from the groups lower in the triangle.

Fibre is not digested; it is stored as **faeces** in the **rectum** and **egested** by the **anus**.

salivary gland

gullet

Digested food is absorbed through the walls of the small intestine.

The large intestine removes water from undigested food.

Water is added to the dried foods before they are eaten. The plant foods that are grown on board need to be eaten raw, since preparing and cooking vegetables is difficult in a weightless environment. Quinoa plants (pronounced '*keen-wa*') have leaves and seeds that can be eaten raw. The seeds contain a good supply of **carbohydrates**, **proteins** and **fats**. Carbohydrates are needed for energy. Proteins are needed for growth and repair. Fats are used as a store of energy and to help keep the body warm.

A quinoa plant.

The plants grown on board will also have another benefit. They will produce oxygen which is needed for **aerobic respiration**. The word equation for anaerobic respiration is:

glucose + oxygen ⟶ carbon dioxide + water (+ energy)

Carbon dioxide dissolved in the plasma goes into the alveolus to be exhaled.

Oxygen from inhaled air enters the capillary and is carried in red blood cells.

these muscles (called **intercostal muscles**) push the ribs out

the **diaphragm** moves downwards

breathing in (**inhalation**)

the **intercostal** muscles relax

the **diaphragm** rises

breathing out (**exhalation**)

The lungs have a **large surface area** because they contain a lot of **air sacs**. Air sacs contain many small pockets called **alveoli**.

plasma

to the heart to be pumped around the body

carbon dioxide

oxygen

red blood cell

*Moving air into and out of the lungs is called **ventilation**. The movement of the muscles is called **breathing**.*

An alveolus.

Oxygen enters the body through the **lungs** and is carried around the body by **red blood cells**.

Air containing oxygen is stored in tanks in the astronaut's back pack.

The glucose is dissolved in the blood **plasma**. Cells in the body get the glucose and oxygen they need for respiration from the blood. More oxygen and glucose will be used up when an astronaut has to do something energetic like a 'space walk'. Space walks will be needed to fix things that go wrong on the outside of the spacecraft.

1 a) Name the seven food groups needed in a balanced diet.
 b) What does the body use each of these for?

2 a) What chemicals does the body produce to digest food?
 b) Name two places where these chemicals are used to digest food.
 c) Why does food need to be digested?
 d) Where is the digested food absorbed into the blood?
 e) What happens to undigested food?

3 a) Write out the **word equation** for aerobic respiration.
 b) What are the **reactants** in aerobic respiration?

4 a) Explain why an astronaut needs to use more glucose during a space walk.
 b) What will happen to the astronaut's **breathing rate** during a space walk? Explain your answer.
 c) How are the lungs **adapted** to absorb a lot of oxygen from the air?

5 Why do you think smoking will not be allowed on board the spacecraft? Give two reasons.

How will the plants be grown on board the spacecraft?

The plants grown on the spacecraft will provide food for the astronauts. The plants will also use up the carbon dioxide produced by the astronauts' respiration and will produce oxygen. They do this using **photosynthesis**. This is the word equation for photosynthesis:

$$\text{carbon dioxide} + \text{water} \; (+ \text{ light energy}) \longrightarrow \text{glucose} + \text{oxygen}$$

Wheat plants growing on board MIR.

However, the plants use up some of the oxygen they produce because they also carry out aerobic respiration to release energy in their cells.

The plants that are grown need to be small since there is not much room. The light that they need will have to be provided by lamps, so plants that can grow quickly without needing too much light should be used. The **biomass** that they produce will need to contain a lot of **nutrients** and most of it will need to be edible. There is no point growing plants that have large parts that cannot be eaten.

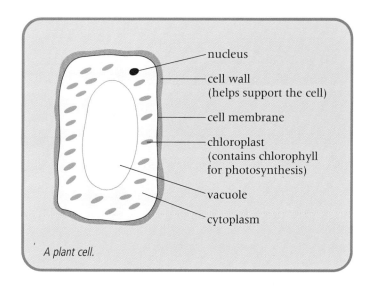

A plant cell.

- nucleus
- cell wall (helps support the cell)
- cell membrane
- chloroplast (contains chlorophyll for photosynthesis)
- vacuole
- cytoplasm

PGC 2 BPAC
FRONT/FLIGHT

These cabinets are like the ones which will be used on the spacecraft to Mars.

Scientists are developing plants that can be grown in space. One way of doing this is through **selective breeding**.

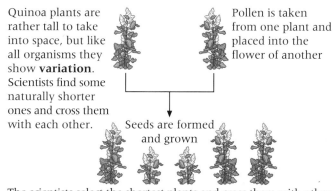

Quinoa plants are rather tall to take into space, but like all organisms they show **variation**. Scientists find some naturally shorter ones and cross them with each other.

Pollen is taken from one plant and placed into the flower of another

Seeds are formed and grown

The scientists select the shortest plants and cross them with other short quinoa plants. If they do this over and over again, eventually they will end up with a new short **variety** of quinoa plant.

How scientists might selectively breed quinoa plants.

The plants will be grown in water, without any soil. The water will contain all the **mineral salts** that they need (like nitrates which are needed to make proteins). These mineral salts will have to be carried on board.

Water that evaporates into the air from the growing plants will be collected by a special water collecting unit. As much water as possible needs to be reused so that only a little needs to be taken on board.

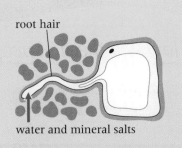

Water and mineral salts are absorbed by a plant using root hair cells. The cells are adapted to their function by having a large surface area.

root hair

water and mineral salts

The water collecting unit will also purify the astronauts' urine and they can drink the water made from it. The astronauts' faeces could be used as plant fertiliser!

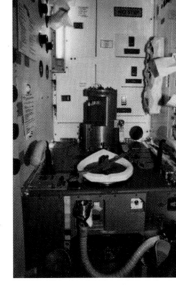

A space loo.

1 a) Write out the word equation for photosynthesis.
   b) Where will the light needed for photosynthesis come from on board the spacecraft?
   c) What chemical in plant cells absorbs the light energy so that photosynthesis can happen?
   d) What other process happens in the cytoplasm of plant cells all the time?
   e) What problem might this process cause if there is a power failure on board?

2 Name four chemical *elements* needed for plant growth.

3 a) What is the function of root hair cells?
   b) How are they adapted to this function?

4 a) List three uses of water on board the spacecraft.
   b) Why is it important that most of the water is recycled?

5 List three things that scientists could selectively breed for when developing new plant varieties to take on long space missions.

6 One plant that has already been grown in space is a variety of lettuce. Why do you think this is a good plant to grow on board? (Hint: How much of the plant can be eaten?)

How will the first people on Mars grow crops?

apple trees

potatoes

lettuces

Robots will be sent ahead of the astronauts to build their living quarters.

Only simple vegetables that can be eaten raw can be grown on the spacecraft. Plants like potatoes and wheat, which need cooking but are very rich in carbohydrates, could be grown in the greenhouses on Mars. They might even grow fruit trees. Fruit trees are adapted to the seasons on Earth and so drop their leaves in autumn (a **seasonal change**). Mars also has seasons but each one lasts about six months.

The people on Mars will need to create artificial **habitats** in the greenhouses for the plants to grow in. The table shows how the plants will get the things they need to grow.

What the plants need	How they will get it
Light	Mars gets only 43% of the sunlight that we get on Earth The plants will need to be ones that are adapted to grow with less light
Carbon dioxide	The atmosphere of Mars contains 95% carbon dioxide
Water	Scientists think they may be able to mine this
Warmth	Mars is very cold (it has a mean temperature of about −60 °C!) but the Sun shining on the greenhouses will warm them up
Mineral salts	The soil on Mars contains enough of these

An asparagus plant growing on soil made from Martian rocks.

Dr. Michael Mautner has grown asparagus and potato plants using rocks from Mars. The plants grew better in some Martian rocks than others. This is because different rocks contain different amounts of mineral salts. This causes **environmental variation** in the plants.

The first people on Mars will not eat animals. This is because most of the chemical energy stored in food is lost at each step along a **food chain**.

If water is discovered below the surface of Mars, the astronauts may build a pond and take simple pond animals with them to see how well they survive on Mars.

An organism's surroundings are called its **environment**. This contains **physical factors** (eg amount of light) and **living factors** (ie other living things). **Variation** caused by environmental factors is called **environmental variation**. The area where an organism lives is called its **habitat** (eg pond, greenhouse).

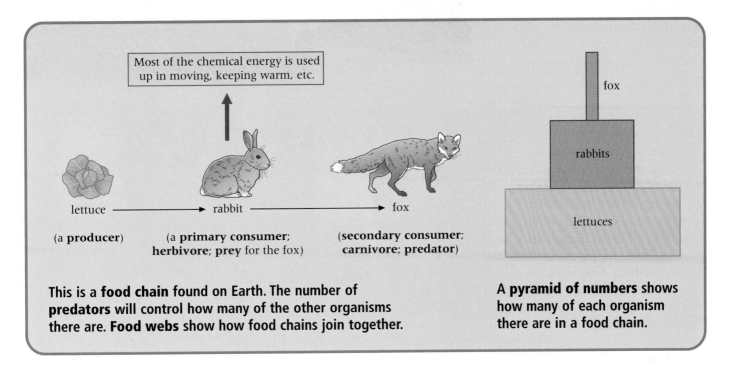

Most of the chemical energy is used up in moving, keeping warm, etc.

lettuce ⟶ rabbit ⟶ fox

(a **producer**) (a **primary consumer**; herbivore; **prey** for the fox) (**secondary consumer**; carnivore; **predator**)

This is a **food chain** found on Earth. The number of **predators** will control how many of the other organisms there are. **Food webs** show how food chains join together.

A **pyramid of numbers** shows how many of each organism there are in a food chain.

fox

rabbits

lettuces

1 a) Look at the food chain above. What does it tell you?
  b) Write out a food chain, involving humans, found on Earth.
  c) Write out a food chain, involving the first humans on Mars.
  d) Explain why the food chain on Mars needs to be much shorter.

2 a) List the things that plants need to be able to grow.
  b) How will the amount of sunlight on Mars affect the speed of growth of the plants? Explain your answer.

3 Look at the picture at the top of the previous page.
  a) What habitat will the plants grown on Mars be in?
  b) A **community** is all the organisms living in a habitat. Name the organisms in this community.
  c) What is the environment around one of the lettuce plants made up of?

4 An apple tree on Earth keeps its leaves for six months. How many months do you think an apple tree on Mars would keep its leaves for? Explain your answer.

5 It is important that any seeds planted do not contain weed seeds. Explain why. Use the word **compete** in your answer.

Life and living on Mars

Why is there no life on the surface of Mars?

The first people to live on Mars will be scientists. They will try to discover whether there is, or ever has been, life on Mars. In 1996, some scientists found things in a rock from Mars which they suggested were very small fossilised bacteria.

The rock from Mars

Are the things that have been coloured blue fossilised Martian bacteria? They are much smaller than normal bacteria and scientists can't decide.

Bacteria are a type of **microbe**. Other microbes include **viruses** and some **fungi** (eg yeast). Some microbes are harmful (they cause disease); others are useful and we use them to make things (eg bread). Bacteria and fungi are in different **kingdoms** (the other kingdoms are plants, animals and protoctists). Kingdoms are divided up into smaller groups (eg the animal kingdom contains **vertebrates** and **invertebrates**).

There is no life on the surface of Mars. There is no water or oxygen and too much ultraviolet light (on Earth we are protected from this by the ozone layer). The Martian atmosphere is very thin and contains 95% carbon dioxide with some argon and nitrogen. However, some scientists think that there might be water underground with bacteria living in it.

Scientists are designing ways of making Mars become like Earth. This is called 'terraforming', but it may take up to 1000 years! In the meantime, we could build cities under protective domes and by 2100 many people might live like this.

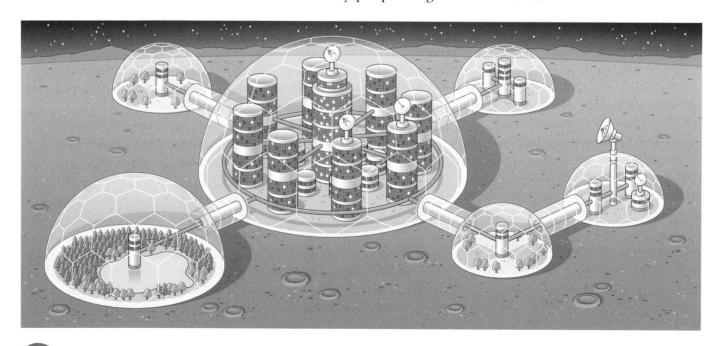

If there is underground water on Mars, lakes could be formed in which fish could be grown as food. Trees could be grown and the wood used. Any area where the trees are cut down would need to be replanted. **Sustainable development** would be very important.

Like children born on Earth, children born on Mars will have **inherited variation** which will make them all look different. However, with $\frac{1}{3}$ less gravity on Mars, the children may grow taller than they would on Earth (an example of environmental variation).

During the next decade many unmanned missions will go to Mars. These missions will help us to work out whether living on Mars is a realistic possibility.

> **Inherited characteristics** are controlled by **genes** found on **chromosomes**. Genes from different parents are mixed in **sexual reproduction** when a **sperm cell** and an **egg cell fuse** with each other at **fertilisation**. It takes about 12–13 years for humans to become capable of reproducing. At this point **puberty** occurs and changes take place in the body (eg enlargement of **penis and testes** in males and enlargement of **breasts** in females). In women, the **menstrual cycle** also begins. This cycle causes the lining of the uterus to get thicker over the course of a month and then break down (**menstruation**). An egg cell is released in the middle of this cycle. If the woman becomes **pregnant** the developing baby is given the things it needs (like oxygen and food) via the **placenta**, which is attached to the baby by the **umbilical cord**.

1 a) Name two kinds of microbe.
  b) Give two uses of microbes.

2 To terraform Mars, oxygen needs to be added to the atmosphere. Suggest a simple way of doing this.

3 a) What is sustainable development?
  b) Why will the sustainable development of woods be important in a Martian city?

4 Explain how people inherit characteristics from their parents.

5 a) If there are living bacteria on Mars, they would only live underground. Why?
  b) To be living, an organism must carry out the seven life processes. Name these.
  c) If there are living bacteria on Mars, do you think they will use aerobic or anaerobic respiration? Explain your answer.

6 a) List three changes that occur in a boy at puberty.
  b) List three changes that occur in a girl at puberty.

7 a) Name two things that a developing baby in the uterus needs to get from the mother.
  b) Name one waste product that is removed from the developing baby.
  c) How are substances given to and taken away from the developing baby?

6 Write a short story about what living in a Martian city, like the one on the previous page, would be like.

All living things **respond** to changes in their surroundings. The things that they respond to are called **stimuli** (singular = **stimulus**). Humans have cells, called **receptors**, that detect stimuli. The things that our receptors detect are often called our 'senses'. Most people think we only have five senses. In fact, we have six!

Stimulus	Where the receptor cells are found
Light	Eye
Sound	Ear
Touch	Skin
Taste	Tongue
Smell	Nose
Change in body position (our sense of balance)	Ear

We all need to respond to stimuli. In most cases, the information about the stimulus is carried from the receptor cells, along nerves, to the brain. Information is sent along nerves as 'electrical messages' called **impulses**. Your brain then 'decides' what to do.

For instance, receptor cells in your ears may detect a sound from a radio and the information is sent to your brain. Your brain turns this information into sound which you hear. If you don't like the song, your brain may send impulses along nerves down to the muscles which move your hand to switch the radio off. The parts of your body that receive these impulses are called **effectors**. The muscles in your hand are the effectors in this example.

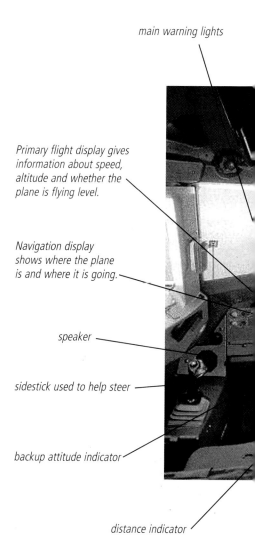

main warning lights

Primary flight display gives information about speed, altitude and whether the plane is flying level.

Navigation display shows where the plane is and where it is going.

speaker

sidestick used to help steer

backup attitude indicator

distance indicator

An Airbus 320.

How quickly you respond to a stimulus is known as a **reaction time**. Fast reaction times are often very important when flying an aeroplane. It is important for the pilots to know about a problem straight away so they can respond to it quickly. Aircraft designers spend a great deal of time making sure that pilots will be able to get information about a problem quickly. For instance, the warning lights are straight in front of the pilots since they may not be noticed quickly enough if they were behind the seats! The designers also make sure that all the displays can be easily read.

A Lockheed F-117A Stealth Fighter.

Ground proximity warning system informs pilots if they get too close to the ground, by 'speaking' to them.

fuel display panels

Some war planes have a display showing the ground.

The flight deck of an Airbus 320.

engine display screens

The cockpit of a Lockheed F-117A Stealth Fighter.

Playing arcade games also demands quick responses to stimuli.

P Recording reaction times

A simple way to measure reaction times is for one person to hold a metre ruler up. They drop it and another person has to catch it.

The reaction time can be worked out using a graph or this equation:

$$t = \sqrt{\frac{d}{490}}$$

d = distance the ruler fell in cm
t = reaction time in seconds

Another way is to use an electrical circuit and timing device. Switching on one switch should start the timing device and turn on a lamp or a buzzer. Another switch should be operated by the person whose reaction time you are measuring. When the person sees the lamp come on, they press their switch and this stops the timer.

- Design a circuit which could measure reaction times.
- Compare the results you get when using the circuit and the ruler method.
- Explain any differences in the reaction times recorded in each method.

P What stimulus?

Find out which sort of stimulus (for example, light or sound) gives the shortest reaction time.
- Which method will you use – dropping a ruler, or a circuit?

- Use your findings to suggest how warning signals should best be given to pilots.
- Where should the objects giving the warning signals be placed on the flight deck?

P Red for warning?

It is traditional to use red lights for warning, but does this colour give the fastest reaction time?
- If you use the circuit method, you could use a circuit with different coloured bulbs.

If you use the ruler method, build a simple circuit containing a coloured light bulb. The person who drops the ruler should switch the circuit on at the same time as dropping the ruler.

Flight Sim

Flight simulator arcade games often play music. Does this speed up or slow down reaction times? You could try measuring reaction times:
- with and without music
- with different sorts of music
- with the same music played at different volumes.

Use your results to suggest to an arcade games manufacturer how to make their flight simulator game more difficult.

Sight problems

Find out about people with visual impairments.
- How can these people read? Find out about Braille and/or the Moon system.
- How do these people watch TV? Find out about 'audio description'.
- Are there different types of visual impairment?

This person is an 'audio describer'.

Reflex actions

Find out what a **reflex action** is.
- Try to find out at least four examples in the human body.
- Why do doctors test reflex actions?
- Why are reflex action times faster than normal reaction times?

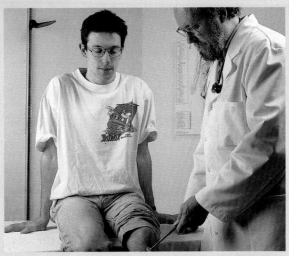

When the area just beneath the knee cap is tapped, the lower leg swings out automatically. This is called the 'knee-jerk' reaction.

Hearing problems

Find out about people with hearing difficulties.
- How can these people watch TV? Find out about subtitling.
- How can deaf people talk to each other? Find out about British Sign Language.

This person is a subtitler.

Fruits, like apples, contain a substance called **pectin**, which helps to hold cell walls together. As the fruit ripens, an **enzyme** called **pectinase** is produced which starts to break apart the pectin.

Pectinase can be used to make apple juice. If it is added to mashed up apples, the cell walls break apart. When the mashed up apples are pressed, more juice can be squeezed out. This means that the apple juice company can make more money!

Enzymes like pectinase can be added to help break apart the cell walls of apples so that more juice can be extracted.

Something else happens when apples ripen. They get sweeter. This is due to another enzyme called **amylase** which breaks down the starch stored in the apple and turns it into sugars. The sugars taste sweet. Adding amylase to the mashed apples can make the apple juice sweeter.

Apple juice is often cloudy after it has been squeezed, since there are insoluble bits in it. To make clear apple juice, more pectinase (and other enzymes) can be added to break apart the insoluble bits and turn the juice clear.

The cloudiness in apple juice can be removed using pectinase.

Sometimes you see ready-peeled oranges for sale. These have not been peeled by some poor person slaving away for hours peeling oranges! Pectinase is used to do the peeling. Cuts are made in the peel and the fruit is then placed in a solution containing pectinase. The fruit is then put into a machine called a 'vacuum infuser'. This machine sucks all the gases out of the space between the flesh and the peel and so the pectinase gets inside. Here, the pectinase gets to work and breaks down the pectin in the white part of the peel. After about 30 minutes, the fruit is removed and the peel almost falls off!

These people are simply twisting the peel off the fruit in the lower tray and putting it into the upper tray.

These bananas are being ripened using ethene.

The ripening of fruits is controlled by **plant hormones**. These are produced by the fruits themselves and cause the ripening enzymes to be produced. One plant hormone is a gas, called **ethene** (or ethylene). We use ethene to ripen many of the fruits in supermarkets. Bananas are picked green and unripe in the Caribbean and shipped to the UK. Here they are stored in warehouses. Ethene is pumped into the warehouses and the bananas ripen and turn yellow.

Cut flowers also ripen! They produce ethene which causes the enzymes to start to work. The enzymes make the stem go soft and start to rot. Cut flowers are often put into water that has chemicals added to stop the enzymes working. Bouquets are often sold with sachets of these chemicals.

Making apple juice

Cellulase is an enzyme that breaks apart the cellulose in cell walls. Will it be better than pectinase at making apple juice from apple sauce? How would you find out?

- How will you measure how good the enzymes are at making apple juice?
- How long will you leave your experiment for?
- How will you make your investigation a fair test?
- You could also see if using boiled enzymes has the same effect.
- Your teacher might have other enzymes you could investigate.

apple sauce

distilled water

cellulase solution

pectinase solution

Pectinase activity

A clear apple juice manufacturer wants to make sure that pectinase is working at its best. What are the **optimum conditions** for pectinase?

- You could alter the temperature, the pH or the amount of pectinase.
- Remember, you will not be able to drink your apple juice so it does not matter if you want to add laboratory acids or alkalis.
- How will you judge the cloudiness of your juices?

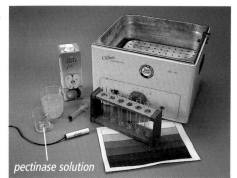

pectinase solution

Ripe tomatoes

Many people leave unripe tomatoes on a brightly lit window sill to ripen. Some people put unripe tomatoes in a drawer with a ripe one. How would you find out which way is best? You could use tomatoes or bananas or any other unripe fruits.

- Does having a ripe fruit next to an unripe one speed up ripening?
- Does light speed up ripening?
- You could put fruits in sealed black or clear plastic bags, or leave them in the open.
- Will you have the fruits touching each other or not?

P **Keeping flowers fresh**

Some people put aspirin into the water that cut flowers are placed in. Other people put copper coins into the water. Do either of these methods actually make the flowers last longer?

- What flowers will you use? Dandelions are normally in plentiful supply and you won't need to pay for them!
- Are there any other chemicals you could try adding to the water?

Growing towards light

These seedlings are growing towards the light from the side.

Find out why this happens.

- What plant hormone does this?
- How does this hormone allow the seedling to grow towards the light?
- Why do gardeners use hormone rooting powders for cuttings?

Enzymes and food

Enzymes are used in the manufacture of all sorts of foods. Find out about one use of an enzyme in making food. You can choose one of the things from the photographs below or something else. You will need to say:

- what food is being made
- what enzyme is being used
- where the enzyme comes from
- what the enzyme does.

What kind of soil do you have?

Soil is a mixture of different materials such as rock particles, **humus** (the decayed remains of plants and animals) and water.

The materials in soil make some soils more acidic or alkaline than others. We can measure the pH of the soil. The pH scale tells us how acidic or alkaline the soil is.

If the pH is less than 7, the substance is acidic. If the pH is equal to 7, the substance is neither acidic nor alkaline, it is neutral. If the pH is more than 7, the substance is alkaline.

We can test the pH of a sample of soil by dipping a piece of indicator paper into a mixture of the soil and water, or by adding some universal indicator solution to the soil and water mixture.

Soil testing kits are often sold by garden centres so that gardeners can find out the pH of their soil.

1 Make a list of the materials which are found in soil.

2 How can we measure the pH of a soil sample?

3 What does the pH tell us about the soil?

Gardeners and farmers need to know the pH of their soil as many plants prefer to grow in soil with a certain pH. This can be a real problem if the plants that you want to grow don't grow well in your type of soil. The easiest solution to this problem is to grow plants which will survive in your soil conditions.

Collect samples of different soils and examine them carefully using a hand lens. Measure the pH of each sample. Try to find out why some soils are more acidic than others.

The limestone in the soil makes it very alkaline. Only certain types of plants grow well in limestone country.

Hydrangeas will have blue flowers in acidic soils and pink flowers in alkaline soils.

Brussels sprouts grow best in alkaline soils

Azaleas grow well in acidic soils.

If you want to grow plants which don't grow well in your soil, you could try to change the pH.

Acids can be **neutralised** (cancelled out) by adding an alkali. If the soil is acidic, the pH can be increased by adding slaked lime. Slaked lime is calcium hydroxide, an alkali. The alkali neutralises the acid in the soil.

If the soil is alkaline, the pH can be lowered by adding some peat or some well rotted manure.

Some fertilisers can also lower the pH of the soil. This may be a problem if you wish to grow plants which grow best in alkaline soils.

This farmer will spread this slaked lime onto the field.

> **!** *If you want to grow acid-loving plants, you could make the soil more acidic by pouring cold tea on it (without the milk!).*

? 4 a) How can the pH of a soil be increased?
   b) Why does this process increase the pH number of the soil?

5 a) How can the pH of a soil be decreased?
   b) Why does this process work?

You should know...
- About acids, alkalis and neutralisation.
- That the pH of a soil affects the plants that grow in it.
- How the pH of soils can be changed.

How can acids be 'cancelled out'?

Bases are substances that can 'cancel out' acids. Bases which are soluble in water are called **alkalis**.

When a base is added to an acid, a chemical reaction occurs and a new type of chemical compound (a **salt**) is produced. This reaction is called **neutralisation**.

1 a) What is a base?
   b) If a base is able to dissolve in water, what is it called?

If equal amounts of sodium hydroxide and hydrochloric acid are added together, they will completely neutralise each other. A neutralisation reaction takes place and sodium chloride solution is formed which has a pH of 7. The sodium chloride formed in this reaction is an example of a salt and is often known as common salt.

The salt can be obtained from the salt solution by gently heating the sodium chloride and water mixture. The water evaporates, leaving the salt behind.

dilute hydrochloric acid

+

sodium hydroxide solution

sodium chloride solution

Hydrochloric acid + sodium hydroxide ⟶ sodium chloride + water

2 What type of chemical reaction produces a salt?

3 Name two chemicals which would make sodium chloride if they were added together.

4 How can the water and salt be separated?

5 Write a general word equation for the reaction of a base which produces a salt.

6 Write a word equation for the reaction between hydrochloric acid and potassium hydroxide.

Sodium chloride isn't the only salt. Potassium chloride, another salt, is formed when potassium hydroxide reacts with hydrochloric acid. A salt will be formed when any base or alkali reacts with an acid. We can summarise this reaction by writing general equations for neutralisation:

acid + alkali ⟶ salt + water
acid + base ⟶ salt + water

There are many different salts. The first part of the name of a salt is the metal which was part of the alkali. The 'sodium' in sodium chloride comes from the 'sodium' hydroxide used to neutralise the acid.

The other part of the name of the salt tells us which acid was neutralised in the reaction. The table shows which are made from which acids.

chlorides	are made from	hydrochloric acid
sulphates	are made from	sulphuric acid
nitrates	are made from	nitric acid

Different salts are made when different acids are used in neutralisation reactions.

For example:

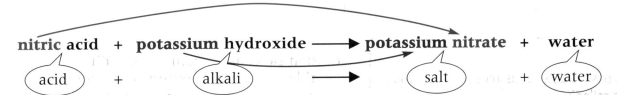

nitric acid + **potassium hydroxide** ⟶ **potassium nitrate** + **water**

acid + alkali ⟶ salt + water

P Which indigestion remedy works best?
Indigestion tablets cancel out acid in the stomach.
• How could you find out which indigestion tablets are best?

Make sure that you carry out a safe investigation!

? **7 a)** Name the salt formed when magnesium hydroxide reacts with hydrochloric acid.
b) What is the other product of this reaction?

8 Name the acid involved in the neutralisation reaction which produced these salts:
a) sodium chloride
b) copper sulphate
c) magnesium sulphate
d) silver nitrate.

9 Choose two of the salts named in question 7 and find out what they are used for. Write a short paragraph about the uses of each of your chosen salts.

You should know...

● **How to obtain a neutral solution from an acid and an alkali.**

● **The general word equations for neutralisation.**

 Neutralisation reactions in your body keep your blood at a pH of between 7.35 and 7.45.

How do insoluble bases react?

Copper oxide is an example of a base which does not dissolve in water. When it is added to sulphuric acid, there is a reaction and copper sulphate is produced.

 +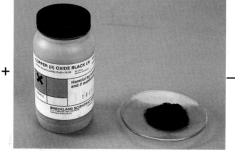

copper sulphate + water

acid   +   **base (metal oxide)** ⟶ **salt + water**

1 Explain why copper oxide is a base but not an alkali.

2 How can you tell that a reaction occurred? What other signs could you have observed if you had carried out this experiment in the laboratory?

3 How could you test to see if the metal oxide has neutralised the acid?

4 Copper sulphate crystals can be made by using copper oxide to neutralise sulphuric acid. Look at the photograph carefully, then describe how you would make copper sulphate crystals from the neutralised solution. What would you need to do before you tried to remove the water? Why?

All metal oxides are bases and will react with acids, although there is not always a colour change to show that this has happened.

Magnesium oxide is a white powder. The salt produced when it reacts with sulphuric acid is also white.

All metal hydroxides and metal carbonates are bases too. Sodium, potassium and ammonium compounds are alkalis as they are soluble in water.

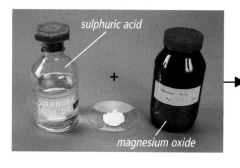

sulphuric acid

magnesium oxide

water

magnesium sulphate

5 Write the word equation for the reaction between magnesium oxide and sulphuric acid.

6 Write the word equation for the reaction between calcium hydroxide and sulphuric acid.

You should know...
- **Insoluble bases also neutralise acids.**

C9c Acids around us

Which acids are in the atmosphere naturally?

The atmosphere around the Earth contains carbon dioxide. Most of the carbon dioxide has been released naturally as living things respire. This carbon dioxide is important to life as it is needed by plants when they carry out photosynthesis. Photosynthesis produces most of the materials that make up plants and these provide food for animals.

The carbon dioxide released during respiration can dissolve in rain, forming a weak acid called carbonic acid. This makes rainwater slightly acidic.

 1 Where has most of the carbon dioxide in the atmosphere come from?

Large quantities of another acidic gas, sulphur dioxide, are released naturally when a volcano erupts.

The molecules of sulphur dioxide in the atmosphere react with more oxygen and dissolve in rain to form a stronger acid, sulphuric acid. After a large volcanic eruption, the pH of the rainwater may become even more acidic.

 2 How does sulphur dioxide get into the atmosphere naturally?

3 Name two acids which make rain acidic.

 4 The pH of rainwater is normally between pH 5.6 and pH 5.8. Suggest a value for the pH of rainwater in a region where a volcano has recently erupted.

You should know...

- The atmosphere contains carbon dioxide from natural sources.
- Volcanoes release sulphur dioxide.
- These gases dissolve in rainwater, making it slightly acidic.

How does human activity cause acid rain?

Rain is naturally slightly acidic because carbon dioxide and sulphur dioxide dissolve in it. Extra carbon dioxide is released into the atmosphere when we burn fossil fuels. Most fossil fuels contain an impurity called sulphur as well as carbon. When this sulphur is burned, extra sulphur dioxide is released into the atmosphere.

Nitrogen oxides are acidic gases, released by car engines. They also dissolve in rain. The nitrogen oxides and the extra carbon dioxide and sulphur dioxide dissolve in rain and can make it very acidic. When the pH of rain falls below 5.6 it is called **acid rain**.

Acid rain falling on Scandinavia has made some lakes so acidic that fish are killed. Large quantities of crushed limestone can be added to neutralise the acid in the lake. Limestone is a base called calcium carbonate.

Acid rain damages living organisms. It also reacts with some stones and corrodes some metals.

 In 1983, rain with a pH of 1.87 fell on Inverpolly Forest, Scotland.

 1 Name three gases that can dissolve in rain to make it acidic.

The acid in the air has reacted with this stone sculpture in Cracow, Poland.

Acid rain affects living organisms as well as materials.

 How does acid rain affect different materials?
Investigate the effect of acid rain on a variety of materials.
- Are all materials affected by acid rain?
- Are some affected more than others?
- How quickly does the reaction take place?
- How will you measure the changes in the materials you investigate?

There are ways to reduce the amount of acid rain in the environment.

Large coal-burning power stations, which release sulphur dioxide, can be fitted with scrubbers and flue gas desulphurisation plants which remove the sulphur dioxide.

This power station has been fitted with a flue gas desulphurisation plant which removes the sulphur dioxide before it reaches the atmosphere.

We can control the quantity of nitrogen oxides, sulphur dioxide and carbon dioxide released by burning smaller amounts of fossil fuels and using alternative forms of energy, such as wind and solar power instead.

A wind farm in California. Smaller ones can be found in Britain, for example in the Lake District.

 2 What are the effects of acid rain on the environment?

Nitrogen oxides, from hot engines, can be prevented from reaching the atmosphere by using a **catalytic converter**.

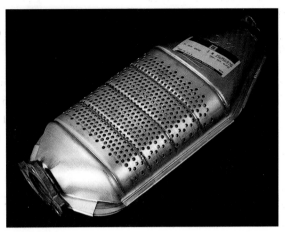

A catalytic converter changes the car exhaust gases into nitrogen, carbon dioxide and water.

 3 Describe three different ways of reducing acid rain production.

4 Why is it impossible for rain to be neutral?

5 Cars with catalytic converters still produce an acid gas. What gas do they produce?

6 Find out what the World Solar Challenge is. Who won the competition the last time it was held?

You should know...

- **Burning fossil fuels releases sulphur dioxide and carbon dioxide.**
- **Hot car engines release nitrogen oxides.**
- **These gases dissolve in rain to form acid rain.**
- **The effects of acid rain and how to reduce acid rain formation.**

How can acid affect rocks?

Some rocks, such as limestone, chalk and marble, react with acids. These rocks all contain calcium carbonate. All carbonates react with acids, producing a salt as one of the products. The calcium carbonate in rocks reacts with the acid and new chemicals are made, leaving a smaller, **weathered** piece of rock behind.

The limestone wall of this cottage has been weathered by the action of slightly acidic rain falling on it for many years.

 1 What is the name of the chemical in limestone which reacts with acid?

 Design an experiment to find out what happens when a carbonate is added to some dilute acid.
- How will you know if there has been a reaction?
- What observations will you record?
- How could you find out what the products are?

You could try different carbonates, such as sodium carbonate, calcium carbonate and copper carbonate.

When dilute sulphuric acid is added to copper carbonate it begins to fizz.

sulphuric acid

copper carbonate

 2 How do we know that a gas is given off when a carbonate reacts with an acid?

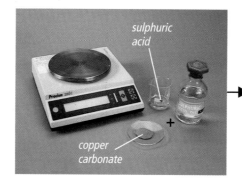

The mixture fizzes because one of the products of the reaction is a gas. The fizz is the gas escaping.

The word 'carbonate' tells us that the compound contains the element carbon, and the ending '-ate' tells us that it also contains atoms of oxygen. When the carbonate reacts, the gas it gives off is carbon dioxide, which contains the elements carbon and oxygen. We can use the limewater test for carbon dioxide to prove that this is the gas which is given off.

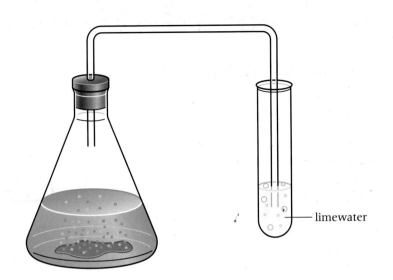
limewater

A salt is also formed in the reaction – copper sulphate. The sulphate comes from the sulphuric acid and the copper comes from the copper carbonate.

3 a) Which gas is produced in this reaction?
   b) How would you test for this gas?

We can write a word equation for the reaction between dilute sulphuric acid and copper carbonate.

sulphuric acid + **copper carbonate** → **copper sulphate** + **carbon dioxide** + **water**

(acid)   (base)   (salt)   (carbon dioxide) (water)

4 What are the products when copper carbonate reacts with nitric acid?

5 Which acid reacts with copper carbonate to produce copper chloride, carbon dioxide and water?

We can also write a general word equation for the reaction between an acid and a carbonate.

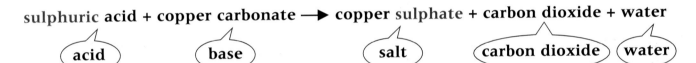

acid + carbonate ⟶ salt + water + carbon dioxide

6 Write word equations for the reaction between sodium carbonate and each of these acids:
   a) sulphuric acid
   b) hydrochloric acid
   c) nitric acid.

You should know...
● Acids react with carbonates to produce carbon dioxide, a salt and water.

How can we make hard water softer?

As rainwater runs over the land it reacts with bases, like calcium carbonate, from the rocks and soil that it passes through. The salts formed by these reactions are dissolved in the water.

Water which has dissolved large amounts of calcium and magnesium salts is known as **hard water**. **Soft water** does not contain as many dissolved salts and feels much smoother when you wash.

Hard water can form stalactites and stalagmites in caves. The water drips very slowly from the roof of the cave and evaporates. The salts left behind form **stalactites** hanging from the roof. Some of the hard water drips onto the floor and evaporates, leaving a **stalagmite** formed from the salts.

1 What does hard water contain?

2 Name one sort of rock that will make hard water when rain water flows over it?

Hardwater has formed these stalactites and stalagmites in Marakoopa Cave, Tasmania.

When we drink hard water, it helps to supply our bodies with calcium salts which we need in order to develop healthy bones and teeth. It also has a taste which some people prefer.

3 Why do some mineral waters have extra calcium added?

4 Apart from calcium salts, name another type of salt you would expect to find in bottled mineral water.

Bottled mineral water is hard water. Some types have extra calcium salts added.

However, there are disadvantages to living in a hard water area.

When hard water is boiled in a kettle, the salts are left on the inside. The kettle becomes 'furred up'.

Hot water pipes may become so 'furred up' that they are blocked, reducing the amount of hot water which can pass through them.

It is more difficult to make soap form a lather when washing in hard water. This uses a lot more soap and leaves a layer of **scum** on the surface of the water and whatever is being washed.

 5 How can you tell if you live in a hard water area?

Temporary hardness in water can be removed by boiling the water before it is used. This type of hardness is caused by a salt called calcium hydrogencarbonate, formed when rain water reacts with the calcium carbonate in chalk or limestone hills.

Permanent hardness cannot be removed by boiling. It is best removed using an ion-exchange water softener. This removes the calcium and magnesium parts of the salts and replaces them with sodium instead. Water treated in this way should not be used for making baby foods since it contains high levels of sodium salts which may harm the baby.

 6 Describe two ways in which hard water can be softened.

7 a) What salt causes temporary hardness?
   b) Find out what happens to this salt when the water is boiled.

8 Many bathroom cleaners claim to remove 'limescale' in hard water areas.
   a) Find out what limescale is.
   b) What do you think these cleaners contain to get rid of the limescale?

The water is softened as it enters the house.

This filter jug contains an ion-exchange softener which removes the hardness as the water flows through it.

How do metals react with acid?

Most metals will react with an acid, though some unreactive metals will only react very slowly with a strong, concentrated acid and some will not react at all. Other metals are more reactive and explode when added to acid.

When a piece of zinc metal is added to some hydrochloric acid, it reacts, giving off bubbles of gas. Bubbles of gas are also given off when zinc is added to sulphuric acid.

In 1766 Henry Cavendish (1731–1810) added zinc to hydrochloric acid and collected the gas. He identified this gas as a new substance and called it inflammable air. Antoine Lavoisier (1743–1794), gave this gas its modern name of hydrogen.

1 How do we know there is a reaction when we add zinc metal to these acids?

zinc

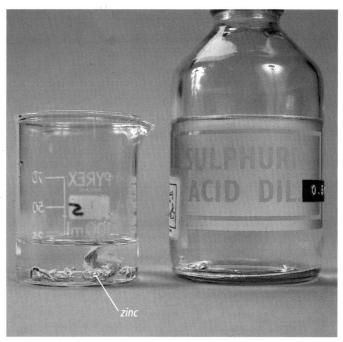
zinc

The same gas is given off in both of these reactions. We can work out what it is by thinking about the chemicals we are reacting together. The table shows the different elements in each chemical.

Formula	Name	Types of atom in substance
Zn	zinc metal	zinc atoms
HCl	hydrochloric acid	1 hydrogen atom and 1 chlorine atom
H_2SO_4	sulphuric acid	2 hydrogen atoms, 1 sulphur atom and 4 oxygen atoms

The only element which is found in both of the acids is hydrogen, so this must be the gas which is given off when the zinc is added.

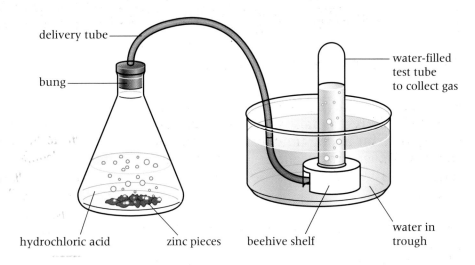

delivery tube

bung

hydrochloric acid

zinc pieces

beehive shelf

water-filled test tube to collect gas

water in trough

This apparatus can be used to collect the hydrogen safely.

We can check this by carrying out the test for hydrogen. If a burning wooden splint is put into the top of a tube of hydrogen gas, the hydrogen burns in the oxygen from the air and explodes with a squeaky 'pop'.

We can write a word equation for this reaction.

hydrochloric acid + zinc ⟶ zinc chloride + hydrogen

acid　　　metal　　　salt　　　hydrogen

2 What is the test for hydrogen gas?

3 Write the word equation for the reaction between zinc and sulphuric acid.

4 What is the general equation for the reaction between a metal and an acid?

5 What do you predict will be made when calcium metal reacts with:
   a) hydrochloric acid
   b) sulphuric acid
   c) nitric acid?

Do other metals react with acids in this way? Find out what happens when magnesium, iron and copper react with hydrochloric acid.
● How can you tell that a reaction has occurred?
● Is a gas produced?
● If so, what is it?
● What else is produced?
Write a word equation for each reaction that takes place.

We can write a general word equation for the reaction between a metal and an acid, although some very unreactive metals (like gold) will not react.

acid + metal ⟶ salt + hydrogen

You should know...

● Some metals react with dilute acids to form salts and hydrogen gas.

● The general word equation:
   acid + metal → salt + hydrogen.

● How to test for hydrogen gas safely.

Why do some metals tarnish?

The medals in the photograph below are made of gold. Gold is a metal which keeps its shiny appearance for a long time. It does not react with the oxygen in the air. It is **unreactive**.

Copper reacts very slowly with the oxygen in the air to form copper oxide, which is black. The older coin is a darker colour because it has a coating of copper oxide on its surface. Copper is slightly more **reactive** than gold.

Sodium is much more reactive than copper. The cut surface of this piece of sodium reacts quickly with the oxygen in the air. After about a minute, the surface of the sodium is no longer shiny and has a pale grey coating. The sodium has been **oxidised**.

1 Name the gas in the air which reacts most easily. Choose from:
oxygen   nitrogen   hydrogen.

2 Name another unreactive metal apart from gold. Choose from:
iron   silver   sodium.

3 How can you tell that the copper in the older coin has reacted with the oxygen in the air?

4 a) Is copper an element or a compound?
   b) Is copper oxide an element or a compound?

5 Copy and complete this word equation:
copper + _____ ⟶ copper oxide

6 What is the chemical name of the pale grey coating on the sodium?

7 Put the three metals copper, gold and sodium in order of reactivity, with the most reactive first.

The pie chart shows the gases that are in dry air. Oxygen is the most reactive gas. Nitrogen is less reactive. Argon does not react at all. Metals usually react with the oxygen in the air.

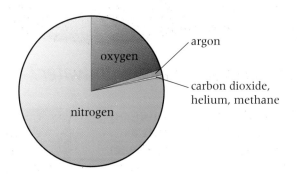

The air is made up of different gases.

P If you had 100 cm³ of air, how much would be used up when metals react? How could you plan an experiment to show this?

Some metals react with oxygen in the presence of water. The iron in the car body has reacted with oxygen to form rust, or iron oxide. Iron is an element. Iron oxide is a compound which contains two elements. The iron oxide takes up more room than the iron on its own, and the rust pushes up the paint and forms 'bubbles' on the surface of the car.

Iron in the car body has reacted with oxygen to form iron oxide, or rust.

The copper in this statue has reacted with oxygen and carbon dioxide to form copper carbonate. This is the green coating.

? 8 Name a gas in the air that is unreactive.

9 If a 1 kg piece of iron was left to rust, would its mass be more, less or the same after it had rusted? Explain your answer.

10 Name the three elements that are in copper carbonate.

11 Write a word equation for the reaction that takes place when copper reacts and gets a green coating.

12 A more accurate description of rust is **hydrated** iron oxide. This tells us that it contains water. One way of writing the formula of rust is $FeO(OH).H_2O$.
   a) There are three elements in hydrated iron oxide. What are they?
   b) What is the total number of atoms of oxygen in this formula?

You should know...
- The meanings of the words reactive and unreactive.
- Some metals are more reactive than others.
- Some gases are more reactive than others.
- When metals react with the oxygen in the air they form oxides.

Which metals react with water?

There is plenty of water on the Earth. Metals such as gold and silver do not react with water and so these metals occur naturally in the environment.

Gold is very rare, and it is also very unreactive. This man is panning for gold in Iquitos, Peru, hoping to find small amounts of gold metal mixed in with the mud and stones at the bottom of the river.

Calcium reacts with water, producing hydrogen gas.

Some metals are much more reactive. Calcium is a reactive metal. It reacts with water, giving off hydrogen gas. The word equation for the reaction is:

calcium + water ⟶ calcium hydroxide + hydrogen

We think of water as a very safe substance, but imagine taking a walk down a street where the paving slabs were made of calcium. As it started to rain, you would hear the hiss of the reaction as the drops of water touched the metal. The ground would start to turn into a white sludge. The heat from the reaction could be enough to burn you. Water would not be a safe chemical in a world made of calcium!

This is why we don't find calcium as an element in the environment. All the calcium in the world is in the form of chemical compounds like calcium carbonate (found in limestone). To make calcium metal, you have to split the calcium from the other elements in the compound using chemical reactions.

?

1 Look at the photograph of calcium in the water. What can you see that tells you that a reaction is happening?

2 From the word equation above, write down the names of:
   a) two elements
   b) two compounds.

3 If you held a lighted splint above the tube, what would happen?

P Calcium reacts with water and the reaction gives off heat. How could you find out what factors will affect the temperature rise?

Potassium is even more reactive than calcium. The heat from the reaction of potassium with water is enough to set the potassium on fire.

When the potassium has finished reacting, the solution can be tested with universal indicator. The purple colour shows that the potassium hydroxide formed in this reaction, is an alkali.

4 a) What colour does the universal indicator go when it is mixed with the potassium hydroxide solution?
  b) Is potassium hydroxide an acid or an alkali?

5 Write a word equation to show the reaction of potassium with water.

Potassium reacts with water even more dramatically than calcium does.

Potassium hydroxide, an alkali, has been formed.

Caesium is the most reactive metal of all. A small piece of caesium placed into water reacts so violently that the container explodes! In general, we can say:

metal + water ⟶ metal hydroxide + hydrogen

Caesium reacts very violently with water.

6 Put the three metals caesium, calcium and potassium in order of reactivity, with the most reactive first.

7 Look at the Periodic Table on page 143.
  a) On which side of the table do you find the reactive metals?
  b) Where do the less reactive metals occur in the Periodic Table?
  c) Where is sodium in the table compared with potassium and caesium?

8 Predict how the reactivity of sodium will compare with:
  a) gold and silver
  b) potassium and caesium.
Explain your reasons.

*Many reactive metals were discovered in the early nineteenth century by Sir Humphry Davy (1778–1829), using the new invention of the battery to pass a current through compounds of the metals. This is an example of the chemical reaction called **electrolysis**.*

You should know...

- Some metals react with water, producing hydrogen gas and a metal hydroxide.
- The most reactive metals are found on the left-hand side of the Periodic Table.
- Less reactive metals are found in the centre of the Periodic Table.

How does temperature affect the reactivity of metals?

Magnesium is quite a reactive metal. It burns with a bright, white flame to leave a white solid ash – magnesium oxide.

Magnesium reacts very slowly with cold water. After a while you might start to see some bubbles on the surface of the metal but it would take several days to collect enough gas to test. Magnesium reacts more quickly with steam. The diagram shows the apparatus that can be used.

Magnesium reacts very slowly with cold water.

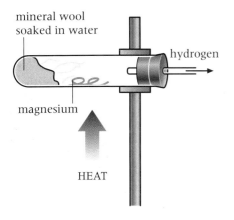

mineral wool soaked in water

hydrogen

magnesium

HEAT

When the tube is heated, the water turns to steam and passes over the hot magnesium. The magnesium starts to glow and it is possible to set light to the gas which comes out of the tube.

The **symbol equation** for this reaction is

$$Mg \ (s) + H_2O \ (g) \longrightarrow MgO \ (s) + H_2 \ (g)$$

1 What gas is formed when magnesium reacts with water?

2 Write the equation for the reaction of magnesium and steam in words.

3 Copy out the symbol equation. Circle the elements and underline the compounds.

4 Explain in your own words why magnesium will react faster with steam than water.

5 The state symbol '(s)' means that the substance is a solid. What do you think the '(g)' means?

6 a) What state is water at room temperature?
  b) Suggest how you might write the formula for liquid water.

7 a) Copy and complete the following table about the symbol equation.

Element	Number of atoms on the left-hand side of the equation	Number of atoms on the right-hand side of the equation
Magnesium	1	
Hydrogen		2
Oxygen		

  b) Use the table to explain in your own words what is meant by saying that the equation is **balanced**.

When is a reactive metal not reactive?

Aluminium is a reactive metal. When aluminium powder is sprinkled into a flame it burns brightly, as it reacts with the oxygen in the air. However aluminium can be left without painting, and it will not corrode in the air.

Imagine a block of aluminium being wrapped in a very thin layer of cling film. You would still be able to see the metal, but the plastic would protect it from attack. Aluminium provides its own protective coating. Aluminium does react with oxygen and a very thin layer of aluminium oxide forms naturally on the surface of the metal. This is insoluble in water, and stops the metal being attacked any more by air or water.

This car has an aluminium body.

It is possible to make this natural layer thicker in a process called anodising. These bars of chocolate have wrappers that are made from anodised aluminium. Dyes can be added during this process to colour the foil.

! *In extreme conditions, the protection breaks down. The aluminium in the* Sir Galahad *burned fiercely when the ship was attacked during the Falklands War.*

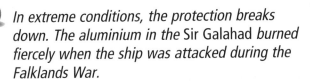

?

1 Write a word equation for the reaction that takes place when aluminium burns.

2 Draw two particle diagrams to show:
   a) the atoms on the surface of a block of aluminium
   b) the same block with a protective coating of oxygen atoms on the surface.
   c) Use your diagram to explain in your own words why aluminium is apparently unreactive.

3 Find out what changes the Navy made to its ships after the *Sir Galahad* caught fire.

Is the order of metal reactivity the same with acids?

Reactions with acids are usually faster than reactions with water. Some metals that do not react with water will react with acids. The photograph shows the reactions of calcium with water and hydrochloric acid.

1 a) Look at the experiment in the photograph. Does calcium react faster with water or with hydrochloric acid?
  b) How can you tell?
  c) Write down three things that would have to be the same in each tube to make this a fair test.

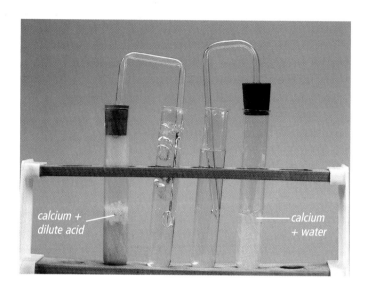

calcium + dilute acid

calcium + water

Although the reaction with acids is quicker, the order of reactivity of the metals is still the same. The metals which are most reactive with water are also the most reactive with acids. Magnesium only reacts slowly with water, but it reacts faster with acid, giving off hydrogen gas. This can be tested using a lighted splint. The hydrogen will burn with a squeaky pop. Calcium is more reactive than magnesium – it reacts easily with cold water. This means that it is likely to react more quickly with acid than magnesium. Here is the word equation for the reaction of calcium with hydrochloric acid:

2 Which metal is more reactive – calcium or magnesium?

3 a) Name the gas given off when metals react with acids.
  b) How can we test for this gas?

calcium + hydrochloric acid ⟶ calcium chloride + hydrogen

- How can you compare the reactivity of metals with acids?
- What will you look for to tell you that a reaction has taken place?
- What factors should you keep the same to make it a fair test?
- Why is it difficult in this case to make the test completely fair?

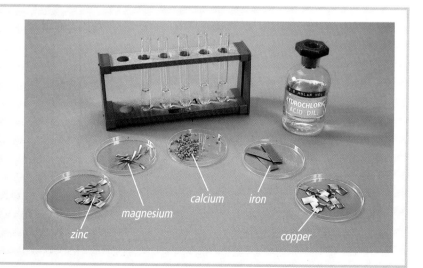

zinc

magnesium

calcium

iron

copper

When metals react with acids, compounds called **salts** are formed. There are many different types of salts. The 'common salt' that you put on your food has the scientific name sodium chloride. The name of each salt has two parts. The first part is the name of the metal used, and the second part comes from the acid. For example, **sulphuric** acid always makes salts called **sulphates**.

In general we can say that:

acid + metal ⟶ salt + hydrogen

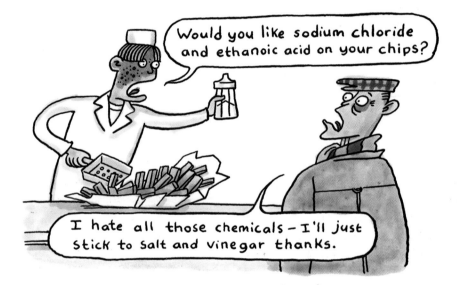

Would you like sodium chloride and ethanoic acid on your chips?

I hate all those chemicals – I'll just stick to salt and vinegar thanks.

You should know...

- Some metals react with acids producing hydrogen, and forming salts.

- The metals that react with water also react very quickly with acids.

- Some metals that don't react with water do react with acids.

4 Copy and complete the table about making salts

Name of acid	Name of salt formed
hydrochloric	chloride
sulphuric	
	nitrate

5 To make common salt from an acid and a metal:
   a) which metal would you use
   b) which acid would you need?
   c) Why would it be very dangerous to try to make salt in this way?

6 Copy and complete these word equations about the reactions of metals with acids.

   (a) zinc + _____ _____ ⟶ zinc sulphate + hydrogen

   (b) iron + hydrochloric acid ⟶ _____ _____ + _____

   (c) _____ + _____ acid ⟶ magnesium nitrate + _____

How can we put metals into a reactivity table?

A football league table ranks teams by giving points for matches won and drawn. Teams that are equal on points are put in order according to goal difference. The **Reactivity Series** of metals is a type of chemical 'league table'. It shows the metals in order, with the most reactive at the top. To decide where a metal comes in the table, we need to look at whether it reacts with oxygen, water and acids. If metals come out equal on this ranking, we would then look at *how fast* they react. The table shows the reactions of metals that you have studied so far.

	P	W	D	L	F	A	Pts
Manchester United.....	8	7	1	0	15	4	22
Liverpool....................	9	6	2	1	16	10	20
Arsenal......................	9	6	2	1	13	6	20
Leeds United..............	9	6	1	1	9	5	19
Bolton........................	9	6	0	3	6	3	18
Chelsea......................	10	5	2	3	10	12	17
Fulham.......................	10	5	1	4	6	4	16
West Ham..................	7	4	1	2	4	9	13
Blackburn..................	9	3	4	2	7	10	13
Charlton....................	8	3	2	3	3	9	11
Newcastle United.......	8	3	0	5	5	12	9

Metal	Reaction with oxygen	Reaction with water	Reaction with dilute acids
Potassium	Burns easily in oxygen with a bright flame	Violent reaction – potassium sets on fire	Dangerously explosive reaction
Sodium		Fast reaction – sodium melts and moves around on the water	
Calcium		Fast reaction with cold water	Very fast reaction, producing hydrogen and heat
Magnesium		Reacts with steam, but only slowly with cold water	Fast reaction
Aluminium	Burns if in fine powder form or if protective coating is broken	No reaction with cold water	Steady reaction
Zinc	Will burn if in powder form		
Iron	Fine wire will react and sparkle when heated. Rusts slowly in moist air		Slow reaction
Lead	Slow reaction to form oxide coating		Very slight reaction
Copper			No reaction
Silver	Very slow reaction		
Gold	No reaction		

The Reactivity Series.

Using different metals, and the acids found in fruits, a small electrical current can be made to flow. This can be used to provide energy for small devices like clocks.

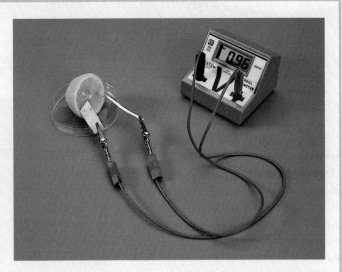

Which pair of metals makes the biggest **voltage**?
- Try out the 'lemon cell' using different combinations of metals.
- Is there a connection between the size of the voltage and the position of the metal in the Reactivity Series?

1 Using the Reactivity Series, give the names of:
   a) two metals that are more reactive than calcium
   b) the least reactive metal
   c) two metals which react with acids but not with water
   d) a metal that does not react with water but does react with steam
   e) two metals that are more reactive than lead and less reactive that aluminium.

2 Use the Reactivity Series to decide whether each of the following will react or not. Write down 'reaction' or 'no reaction'.
   a) gold + dilute sulphuric acid $\longrightarrow$
   b) copper + oxygen $\longrightarrow$
   c) zinc + water $\longrightarrow$
   d) sodium + water $\longrightarrow$
   e) magnesium + hydrochloric acid $\longrightarrow$
   f) lead + water $\longrightarrow$

3 For each of the pairs of substances in question 2 that do react, copy and complete the word equations. You may need to look back over previous pages in the book for help.

You should know...
- Metals can be arranged in order of reactivity.
- The Reactivity Series may be used to predict whether reactions will occur.

How can we use the Reactivity Series to make predictions?

The photograph shows two sections of track being welded together. This is done using a chemical reaction that makes use of the Reactivity Series. Iron oxide is mixed with aluminium powder and heated to start the reaction off. Aluminium is *more reactive* than iron and takes the oxygen from the iron oxide. It **bonds** more strongly with the oxygen and leaves the iron as a free metal. The bonds between aluminium and oxygen are stronger than the bonds between iron and oxygen.

The aluminium has taken the place of the iron. We say that the aluminium has **displaced** the iron. This is a **displacement reaction**. The equation for the reaction is:

aluminium + iron oxide ⟶ aluminium oxide + iron

The reaction produces enough heat to melt the iron, which runs down out of the reaction box into the gap in the rail. As it cools, it welds the sections of rail together.

1 From the word equation on the left, write down the names of:
a) two elements
b) two compounds.

Here is a displacement reaction using a solution. Iron is a more reactive metal than copper. When the iron nail is dipped into the solution of copper sulphate, some copper metal forms on the surface of the iron. Some of the iron goes into the solution to form iron sulphate. The iron has displaced the copper.

copper sulphate solution

copper sulphate solution

2 Using the Reactivity Series on page 68, suggest the name of:
   a) another metal that could be used instead of aluminium to weld tracks together
   b) a metal that would not react with iron oxide to produce iron
   c) a metal that would displace lead from a solution of lead chloride.

3 Write a word equation for the reaction between iron and copper sulphate.

4 In the reaction between iron and copper sulphate, which metal:
   a) forms a compound
   b) starts in a compound and becomes a free element?

The general rule is that the more reactive metal will bond more strongly with the non-metal. The less reactive metal will be left on its own as the free element. Here is an example which shows iron displacing lead:

lead   oxide   +   iron   →   iron   oxide   +   lead

P How can you use the Reactivity Series to predict whether a metal will react with a solution of a compound?
● What would you do to test your predictions?

magnesium sulphate solution

5 In the reaction between iron and lead oxide:
   a) which metal bonds more strongly with the oxygen
   b) which metal is less reactive?

6 Use the Reactivity Series on page 68 to predict whether a reaction will occur in each case. Either complete the word equation or write 'no reaction':
   a) magnesium + iron chloride ⟶
   b) magnesium + potassium sulphate ⟶
   c) iron + calcium oxide ⟶
   d) zinc + copper nitrate ⟶
   e) copper + silver nitrate ⟶

You should know...
● **That more reactive metals can displace less reactive metals from their compounds.**

What properties do the materials around us have?

The Forth Rail Bridge was built using 55 000 tonnes of steel. This metal was chosen because it was a solid which was strong enough to carry the weight of the trains going across it.

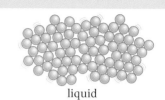
liquid

Water is a liquid. Liquids...

- **have particles that are held fairly close together by weak bonds**
- **cannot be squashed**
- **flow quite easily**
- **have a fixed volume but no fixed shape**
- **are usually less dense than solids.**

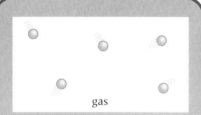
gas

Air is a mixture of gases. Gases...

- **have particles that are well spread out with no bonds between them**
- **are quite easy to squash**
- **flow easily**
- **have no fixed volume or shape**
- **are less dense than liquids.**

The bridge is a solid. Solids...

- **have particles that are held very close together by strong bonds**
- **cannot be squashed**
- **do not flow**
- **have a fixed shape and volume**
- **usually have high densities.**

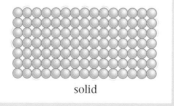
solid

1 Using diagrams, describe the differences between the three **states of matter**, solid, liquid and gas.

2 a) Make a table to show whether each of these are solids, liquids or gases.

    common salt   oxygen
    carbon dioxide   iron
    sand   water

From the list, name:
b) two compounds
c) two elements
d) one soluble substance
e) one insoluble substance.

The railway tracks are also made of steel. When a train runs along the track, friction heats up the wheels and rails. The rails **conduct** this heat away quickly, stopping the wheels and track from getting too hot.

Steel is a **mixture**, mostly made of iron **atoms** but also some carbon atoms. Iron is a **metal element** and carbon is a **non-metal** element.

Metals and non-metals have very different properties.

> **Mixtures** contain different materials jumbled up together but not chemically joined.
>
> **Elements** contain only one sort of atom.
>
> **Compounds** contain two or more sorts of atoms chemically joined together.

Special expansion joints allow the railway track to get longer when it is hot so that the track does not buckle and bend.

Metals...

- are usually solids
- often have high melting and boiling points
- are good conductors of heat and electricity
- can form compounds that are bases when they react with oxygen
- are rigid when thick, but bendy when thin
- can be pulled into thin wires
- in a few cases – iron, nickel and cobalt – they are magnetic.

Non-metals...

- can be solids, liquids or gases
- often have low melting and boiling points
- are poor conductors of heat and electricity
- form acidic compounds when they burn in oxygen
- are usually brittle and break when solid
- cannot be made into wires.

Sea water is also a **mixture**. Water is a **compound**, but sea water contains **soluble** compounds which are **dissolved** in it (like common salt). Moving water can carry **insoluble** materials such as sand.

The air is a mixture of gases, mostly non-metal elements (like nitrogen and oxygen). Other gases in the air are compounds (like carbon dioxide).

Exhaust gases contain carbon dioxide and sulphur dioxide, which are acidic. Sulphur dioxide helps to cause **acid rain**.

3 Describe how you could test a solid material to see if it is a metal or not.

4 Will a magnet stick to the railway tracks? Explain your answer.

5 Explain what happens to the arrangement of iron particles when the railway track gets hotter and colder.

How do the materials around us change?

This house is built from rocks. Rocks can be **weathered** by **chemical reactions** or **physical changes**.

> In a **chemical reaction** new substances are produced.
>
> In a **physical change** no new substances are produced.

The walls are made of limestone (a **sedimentary** rock). The walls are **chemically weathered** by rain, which is slightly acidic. They are also **physically weathered** by changes in temperature which make it expand and contract, making the rock crack. Rocks can also be weathered by plant roots which break the rocks apart as they grow.

The roof of this house is made from pieces of slate. Slate is a fine-grained **metamorphic** rock which contains layers of crystals and can be split into thin sheets.

> **Sedimentary** rock forms when layers of sediment are compressed for a long time.
>
> **Igneous** rocks are formed when magma cools down and becomes a solid.
>
> **Metamorphic** rocks are formed when sedimentary or igneous rocks are put under great pressure at high temperatures.

This gate has been made from iron. Iron is a metal element which reacts with water and oxygen in the air to form iron oxide (**rust**). This chemical reaction is an example of **corrosion**. The gate is being painted to stop it rusting. Paint forms a layer which prevents oxygen and water from getting to the iron.

> Iron can be protected from corrosion by stopping the water and oxygen from getting to it. This can be done by painting, oiling, plating it with a less reactive metal (eg chromium) or galvanising it. When iron is galvanised, it is plated with zinc metal which reacts with the oxygen in the air instead of the iron doing so.

Fuel is burned in a bonfire. The fire will only burn if fuel, heat and oxygen are present.

> A **fuel** is a substance which contains a store of **chemical energy** which can be changed into other forms of energy. Wood, coal, oil and natural gas are all fuels.

We can write a word equation for the bonfire:

fuel + oxygen $\longrightarrow$ carbon dioxide + water (+ energy)

reactants   products

This reaction is called **combustion**, which is an **irreversible** reaction. This means that you can't get back the reactants from the products. It is an example of a **combination** reaction, since the fuel chemically combines with oxygen from the air to produce **oxides** (carbon dioxide and water).

> There are always the same number of each kind of atom before and after a reaction. Afterwards, the atoms are joined in a different way. This is called the Law of Conservation of Mass. Mass cannot be lost or gained during a chemical reaction.

> When natural gas burns in plenty of oxygen, it produces carbon dioxide and water, but if there isn't enough oxygen, it produces carbon monoxide, carbon and water. Carbon monoxide is a poisonous gas which can kill.

---

1 What are the three types of rock and how are they formed?

2 Describe the different ways rocks can be weathered.

3 Are these examples of physical changes or chemical reactions?
   a) limestone being worn away by rain
   b) water turning to steam
   c) coal being burned
   d) rocks being split by plant roots.

4 Which of the changes in question 3 are **reversible**?

5 a) Why does iron rust?
   b) How can rusting be prevented?

6 a) What sort of reaction happens when natural gas burns in plenty of oxygen?
   b) Write a word equation for the reaction.

7 If 6 g of carbon reacts with 16 g of oxygen, what mass of carbon dioxide would be formed?

Where do we find physical and chemical changes in cooking?

The chips are being fried in hot oil. The oil may be at 200 °C. When the chips are placed in the oil they start 'spitting'. Some of the water in the potatoes **evaporates** and turns into steam (water vapour). Steam is invisible, but as it rises into the air it **condenses** again and turns back into tiny drops of water that you can see.

> The **three states of matter** can be changed from one to another.
>
> $$\text{solid} \underset{\text{freezing}}{\overset{\text{melting}}{\rightleftharpoons}} \text{liquid} \underset{\text{condensing}}{\overset{\text{evaporating}}{\rightleftharpoons}} \text{gas}$$

Bread is made from flour and water, with a little sugar, salt, butter and yeast. The yeast use oxygen from the air in the mixture for **aerobic respiration**. This produces bubbles of carbon dioxide which makes the bread rise. This is a chemical reaction. The word equation is:

glucose + oxygen ⟶ carbon dioxide + water (+ energy)

Soda bread is not made using yeast. Instead, sodium hydrogencarbonate is added. This breaks down when heated, forming carbon dioxide bubbles.

Alcoholic drinks such as beer and wine also depend on yeast. This reaction is called **fermentation**. This time oxygen is kept away from the yeast and **anaerobic respiration** takes place to form a type of alcohol called ethanol.

glucose ⟶ ethanol + carbon dioxide

> **Ethanol is flammable.**
>
>
>
> highly flammable

This home-brew kit uses a fermentation lock. This allows the carbon dioxide to escape, but stops any oxygen getting in. The yeast die once the amount of ethanol reaches more than about 15%. Spirits contain about 40% ethanol. Spirits cannot be made by fermentation alone and have to be **distilled**. The mixture is boiled and the vapour condensed. Ethanol boils more easily than water, and so the vapour contains more ethanol than the starting liquid. If you distil wine, you get brandy.

fermentation lock

When you open a jar of coffee you can smell the aroma. Some of the particles of the coffee travel through the air into your nose. This movement of substances is called **diffusion**.

To make 'filter coffee', hot water is poured through coffee powder in the filter. Some of the solid **dissolves** into the water and runs through the filter into the jug. The rest of the powder is **insoluble** and cannot pass through the filter paper. Instant coffee granules are **soluble** and when they are mixed with water they dissolve to make a **solution**.

Milk is a **suspension** of fat in water. The fat partly mixes with the water but does not dissolve.

> **Solute + solvent → solution.**
>
> **Solutions are always clear (transparent), and have only one layer.**
>
> **Insoluble substances will sink or float – there will be layers.**
>
> **Suspensions are cloudy.**

1 a) Which has the higher boiling point – water or cooking oil?
   b) What happens to the water when it is put into hot oil?
   c) What word describes what happens to the steam when it cools down?

2 Write down whether each of these is a physical change or a chemical reaction.
   a) mixing sugar with water
   b) bread mixture (dough) rising
   c) boiling water
   d) fermentation.

3 What does anaerobic respiration not require?

4 What state is coffee in when you can smell it?

5 Use the particle model to explain why the coffee that dissolves in the water passes through the filter paper into the jug.

6 Write down whether the following are solutions or suspensions. Give a reason in each case.
   a) black coffee with no sugar
   b) black coffee with sugar
   c) white coffee with no sugar.

7 The chemical formula for the sugar that you buy in the shops (sucrose) is $C_{12}H_{22}O_{11}$.
   a) There are three chemical elements in sugar – what are their names?
   b) What is the total number of atoms in a molecule of sucrose?

Where do we find chemical changes in the bathroom?

Water is a good **solvent** for many solids. Some liquids (like ethanol) are also soluble in water. Soap can be used to help remove some types of dirt which do not dissolve in water.

The oil in the photograph floats on the water because it is insoluble and less dense than the water. On its own, water is not a good solvent for oil and grease. Soap helps the oil and water to mix together. The lather on the surface shows you that you have enough soap to mix the oil and water together, with some soap left over.

Tube 1

Tube 2

Soaps are made by a reaction using sodium hydroxide. Sodium hydroxide is an alkali and many soaps are also alkalis. Most shampoos and shower gels are made by a reaction using sulphuric acid and most of them have a pH that is less than 7.

This soap is made from the reaction of palm oil and olive oil with sodium hydroxide.

Universal indicator can be used to test the pH of substances. Using universal indicator...

- alkalis give a blue or purple colour and have pH numbers above 7

- acids give an orange or red colour and have pH numbers below 7

- neutral substances, like pure water, give a green colour and are pH7.

Some alkalis and acids can be damaging to your body. They are **corrosive**.

Bases are substances that react with acids. Alkalis are soluble bases.

corrosive

Acids and bases (including alkalis) react in **neutralisation** reactions.

$$acid + base \longrightarrow salt + water$$

Nitric acid gives nitrate **salts**, hydrochloric acid gives chloride salts and sulphuric acid gives sulphate salts.

If you live in a hard water area, it is more difficult to get a lather because minerals in the water react with the soap, forming scum. This reaction does not happen with bubble bath, shower gel or shampoo. This is one reason why many people prefer using these products to soap.

Another chemical that is made from sodium hydroxide is sodium hydrogencarbonate. This foot bath contains a mixture of sodium hydrogencarbonate and citric acid. When the tablets hit the water, a chemical reaction starts and carbon dioxide gas is given off. This makes the water fizzy. After a few minutes all of the tablet has reacted. This is also an example of a **neutralisation** reaction.

acid + carbonate ⟶ salt + water + carbon dioxide

1 a) Explain why water is not good for cleaning greasy stains from clothes.
  b) Apart from using soap or detergents, suggest one other way of getting greasy stains from clothes.

2 a) Describe three differences between the two tubes in the photos of oil and water at the top of page 78.
  b) How can you tell that the oil has mixed better with the water in tube 2?
  c) How do you know that the oil has not completely dissolved in the water?

3 a) What type of substance is sodium hydroxide?
  b) What does 'corrosive' mean?
  c) Explain why dilute sodium hydroxide is less hazardous than concentrated sodium hydroxide.

4 a) Copy and complete the word equation for this reaction:

  _____ _____ + sodium hydroxide ⟶ sodium nitrate + _____.

  b) What sort of reaction is this?
  c) What type of chemical is sodium nitrate?

5 a) Copy and complete the word equation for this reaction:

  sodium hydrogencarbonate + citric acid ⟶ _____ _____ + water + _____ citrate.

  b) Use your understanding of particles to explain why this reaction would take longer in cold water.
  c) Sodium hydrogencarbonate has the formula $NaHCO_3$. How many different elements does it contain?

How are metals obtained and used?

Metals are found in many places in our homes. They are obtained from the Earth. Some metals, like gold and silver, are very **unreactive** and can be found as metals in the earth. Other metals are more reactive and are only found as compounds.

> Some metals are more reactive than others. Metals near the top of the Reactivity Series are more reactive than the ones at the bottom.

Iron is used to make steel for many items in the home, because it is strong and fairly cheap. Iron is found in the earth as iron ore, which is mainly iron oxide. The oxygen has to be removed from the compound before the iron can be used. This could be done by reacting the iron oxide with a metal (such as aluminium) that is higher up the Reactivity Series. The aluminium would **displace** the iron from the oxygen.

> aluminium + iron oxide ⟶ aluminium oxide + iron

Gold.

These knives and forks are made from steel, which is mainly iron.

This reaction would be a very expensive way to produce iron, because you would have to use up a lot of expensive aluminium. Carbon is used instead of aluminium. Carbon is not a metal, but it is more reactive than iron. Carbon is used in a blast furnace to make iron metal from iron oxide.

> A reactive metal will **displace** a less reactive metal from its compounds. This is called a **displacement** reaction.

Aluminium is used to make some saucepans, because it is light. Aluminium is more reactive than iron, and it is also more reactive than carbon. Carbon cannot be used to make aluminium from aluminium oxide. Electrolysis has to be used instead.

Electrolysis can also be used to obtain pure copper metal from a solution of copper sulphate.

Gold and silver are used for jewellery because they are unreactive metals and do not **corrode**. More reactive metals like copper or iron react with oxygen and water in the air. Copper can combine with oxygen in the air to form copper oxide, or combine with oxygen and carbon dioxide to form copper carbonate. Corroded metals can be cleaned using chemicals. Sometimes acids are used to clean metals.

> **Electrolysis breaks compounds apart using electricity. The compound to be split up must be dissolved in water or melted.**

Electrolysis of copper sulphate solution.

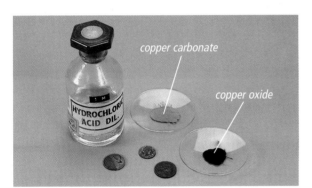

Acid can be used to clean copper coins.

Magnesium reacts vigorously with acid.

The acid reacts with the oxide or carbonate to form a metal **salt**. The metal salt is in solution, and can be washed off the coin. You have to be careful if you are using acids to clean metals. Some metals react with acids to give hydrogen. If you leave the metal in the acid too long, you will end up without a coin at all! More reactive metals can react very fast with acid, so you can't use acid to clean all metals.

> **metal oxide + acid ⟶ metal salt + water**
>
> **metal carbonate + acid ⟶ metal salt + carbon dioxide + water**
>
> **metal + acid ⟶ metal salt + hydrogen**

---

1 Why are metals like aluminium never found in the earth as pure metals?

2 Explain why silver cannot be used to obtain iron from iron oxide.

3 a) How is iron obtained from iron oxide?
   b) Why do you have to use a different method to obtain aluminium from aluminium oxide?

4 How could magnesium be obtained from magnesium oxide? (Hint: there are two possible methods.)

5 Copy and complete these word equations.
   a) iron + silver chloride ⟶
   b) copper oxide + sulphuric acid ⟶
   c) calcium carbonate + hydrochloric acid ⟶
   d) magnesium + hydrochloric acid ⟶

What reactions are used in the chemical industry to make new materials?

The chemical industry uses different reactions to produce new materials with useful properties. The raw materials used may be obtained from rocks, from air or from water.

Some materials can be used as they are. Limestone from this quarry can be used directly for building houses or roads.

Lime (calcium oxide) and slaked lime (calcium hydroxide) can be used to neutralise acidity in soil. Lime is also one of the materials needed to make mortar for the building industry. Lime is made by heating limestone strongly. The calcium carbonate in the limestone **decomposes** to form calcium oxide and carbon dioxide.

Aluminium is a light metal which is used for making aircraft and overhead power lines. Aluminium metal is obtained from its ore, bauxite, by passing a large electric current through the molten ore. This process, called **electrolysis**, can be applied to compounds which are dissolved in water or which have been melted so they are liquids.

Fertiliser is produced industrially using a **neutralisation** reaction. The salt ammonium nitrate is used by many farmers and gardeners to supply extra nitrogen compounds to plants. It is produced when nitric acid is neutralised by ammonia.

The thermit reaction.

Ammonia is made from nitrogen and hydrogen using high temperature and pressure inside a tower like the one below. **Synthesis** (combination) reactions occur when two substances combine to form one new compound.

The manufacture of large polymers from monomers obtained from crude oil is also an example of a synthesis reaction.

The thermit reaction produces iron which can be used to weld two lengths of rail together. During this reaction between iron oxide and aluminium, the iron is **displaced** by the more reactive aluminium. The reaction forms aluminium oxide and iron. **Displacement** reactions take place when a more reactive element replaces a less reactive one in a compound.

Calcium sulphate produced in some powerstations can be used to make plaster for the building industry.

The synthesis of ammonia takes place in this tower.

When fossil fuels are burned, sulphur dioxide is released into the atmosphere. Large coal-burning power stations, which release sulphur dioxide, can be fitted with flue gas sulphur precipitation plants. Many of these work by reacting the sulphur dioxide with an alkaline solution made from lime (calcium oxide), forming calcium sulphate. The solid calcium sulphate falls to the bottom of the apparatus, forming a dry **precipitate**. Reactions which produce precipitates are called **precipitation** reactions. Most precipitation reactions happen when two solutions are mixed and give a solid but wet precipitate. The calcium sulphate formed in this reaction can be used to make plaster for the building industry, or as a landfill material for reclaiming land once used by the mining industry.

Limestone

Many compounds, including calcium carbonate, undergo thermal decomposition. The calcium oxide formed has many uses.

What is the connection between limestone and limewater?

- How can you make limewater (calcium hydroxide solution) from calcium oxide?
- Is limewater a good test for carbon dioxide?
- Does limewater still show that carbon dioxide is present if you dilute the limewater by adding more water to it? How much water could you add?
- What happens if you keep blowing carbon dioxide into a tube of limewater? Why does this happen?

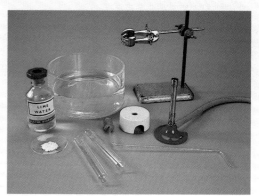

Precipitation

Solid lead iodide is produced during a precipitation reaction between lead nitrate solution and potassium iodide solution. Carry out an investigation to find out about this precipitation reaction.

- How could you measure the amount of lead iodide precipitate formed?
- Does the volume of potassium iodide solution added make any difference to the amount of precipitate?
- Does the temperature affect the amount of precipitate formed?
- Does it matter if the experiment is left overnight before the amount of precipitate is measured?

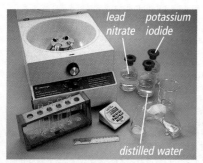

lead nitrate   potassium iodide

distilled water

This apparatus may be useful. Remember to wear eye protection at all times. Lead compounds are poisonous. Make sure you wash your hands thoroughly before putting them or any food into your mouth.

Electrolysis

Pure copper metal can be obtained from a solution of a copper salt, such as copper sulphate, by electrolysis. Which factors affect the amount of copper formed? You could investigate:

- the volume of copper sulphate solution
- the concentration of the copper sulphate solution
- the size of the electric current supplied
- the time that the electric current flows for
- the size of the carbon electrodes.

Apparatus used to electrolyse copper sulphate solution.

Materials from rocks

Many useful products can be obtained from rocks. Some raw materials can be used without chemically changing them.

Other materials can only be obtained from the rock by changing the minerals contained in the rock. Glass is a material which is made from silica, the main component of sand. Glass-making is one of many processes which also needs a supply of limestone.

Choose one material obtained from rocks or minerals.

Granite is quarried and crushed before being used in the construction of roads and as ballast for railway tracks.

- What is the raw material from which the material is obtained? Where is this found? How is it obtained from the earth?
- What is the process used to obtain the useful material from the raw material?
- What is your chosen material used for?

Materials from the air

The air is a mixture of gases, whose exact composition varies from day to day. On a typical day in Britain, the air is made up of the gases shown in the pie chart.

Choose one gas obtained from the air.

- How is it obtained from the air? Are any chemical reactions or physical changes involved?
- What is your chosen gas used for?
- Is your chosen gas used as a raw material to make other useful materials? If so, what?

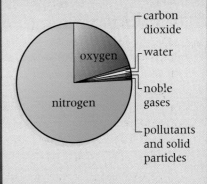

Typical composition of air.

Organic materials

Organic materials come from organisms which are living or were once living. Crude oil is the most important source of organic material for the chemical industry. It is a mixture of many different chemicals which can be separated using a process called fractional distillation.

These objects are all made from plastics.

- How does fractional distillation separate the molecules in crude oil?
- What is cracking? Why is it an important process in the plastics industry?
- What is polymerisation? How are different plastics such as polythene and PVC made? What other plastics are there?
- How are plastics moulded and shaped?

What types of change can take place?

Most chemical reactions involve energy changes. Often this energy is in the form of heat. In many cases the chemicals react together and give out heat into the surroundings. These are called **exothermic** reactions (*exo* = out, *therm* = heat, in Greek).

Other reactions need to take heat in to make them happen. In the laboratory, this heat will usually come from a Bunsen burner. These reactions are called **endothermic**.

mercury chloride solution

Combustion is an exothermic reaction. Fuels react with the oxygen in the air. The heat from the reaction is given out into the room to keep you warm.

Aluminium is normally protected against corrosion. If the protective oxide layer is removed, aluminium reacts very strongly with the oxygen in the air, giving out heat. The protective covering can be removed by dipping aluminium into mercury chloride solution.

Exothermic

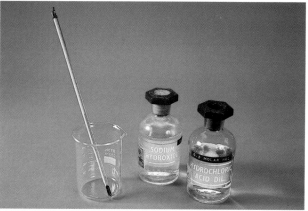

Neutralisation is an exothermic reaction. When an acid reacts with an alkali, the temperature of the solution rises. This excess heat goes out of the beaker and into the air.

Occasionally, chemicals will get *colder* when they react together. This is also an endothermic reaction. Imagine putting your hands around the tube. Heat energy would flow from your hand *into* the tube.

Cracking is an endothermic reaction. Some chemicals from oil are heated so that they split up (or 'crack') into smaller, more useful molecules such as petroleum gases.

Many reactions which give off gases are also endothermic. The chemicals take in some heat from the water, which gets colder. Heat from the room then goes into the glass to warm it up again.

Endothermic

heat energy

Melting is a physical change that is endothermic. Heat goes into the ice cube and turns it into liquid water. Your hand feels cold because it is losing heat energy.

Remember that the energy change is given from the point of view of the *chemicals in the reaction*. In an exothermic reaction, energy is transferred from the chemicals to the surroundings. In an endothermic reaction energy goes from the surroundings into the chemicals.

Energy from fuels

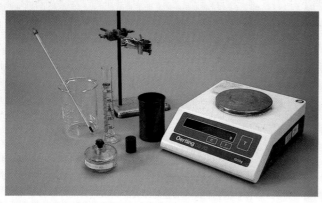

How could you use this apparatus to compare the heat given out by different fuels?
- What would you heat up?
- How would you reduce the amount of heat energy that was wasted?
- What else would you have to do to make it a fair test?

Copper sulphate crystals

Blue copper sulphate crystals have a little bit of water in them. When blue copper sulphate crystals are heated, they turn into a white powder. This is dehydrated (or **anhydrous**) copper sulphate. When you add water to the white powder, the reaction goes back the other way. The solid turns blue, and the chemicals in the tube get hotter.
- Can you find the mixture of water and anhydrous copper sulphate that will give the biggest temperature rise?

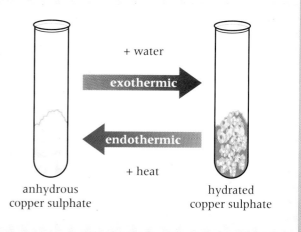

Neutralising acids

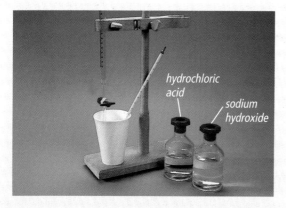

Neutralisation reactions are exothermic. When you react an acid with an alkali, the temperature rises.
- If you keep adding acid, a little at a time, how will you know when the reaction has finished?
- Which acid and alkali will give the biggest temperature rise?

Alfred Nobel

Explosives are extremely exothermic reactions. Dynamite is a powerful explosive. Research the life and work of Alfred Nobel, and find out how the 'bringer of death' was also responsible for setting up the famous Peace Prize.

Sports packs

Sports injuries can be treated with heat (provided by heat packs) or with cold (provided by cool packs). Heat packs are also used by walkers or golfers to keep them warm on cold days.

- Find out how and when you would use heat packs or cold packs on a sports injury, and what precautions you would need to take.
- Find out how heat packs and cold packs work, and if there are any chemical reactions involved.

Ethanol and engines

We depend heavily on the exothermic reaction between petrol and air to provide the energy for our transport. The heat from the burning fuel is converted into kinetic energy.

- How is a diesel engine different from a petrol engine? In what ways is it the same?
- In Brazil, they use a mixture of ethanol (a kind of alcohol) and petrol to power their cars. Find out how the ethanol is made. Could we use this method in Britain?
- Would battery-powered cars solve the problems of a possible shortage of petrol in the future?
- Some vehicles now run on hydrogen. How does a hydrogen-powered car work?

P9a Forces in motion

What are the effects of balanced and unbalanced forces?

Forces are pushes or pulls. The unit for measuring force is the **newton (N)**. Forces working in opposite directions are **balanced** if they are the same size. They are **unbalanced** if they are different sizes.

Unbalanced forces can cause three things to happen. They can change the *speed* of something, the *direction* it is travelling, or its *shape*.

There are several forces acting on moving cars. There is a forward force from the engine, and backwards forces from **friction** and **air resistance** (sometimes called **drag**). The combined result of these forces is called the **resultant** force.

If the forwards force is greater than the backwards forces, the resultant force will be forwards and the car will **accelerate** (or speed up). If the forwards force and backwards force are the same size then the forces are balanced. The resultant force is zero and the car will travel at a steady speed.

Drag racing cars are slowed down with parachutes.

1 a) What forces are acting on the drag racing car in the bottom photograph?
   b) Are the forces balanced or unbalanced? Explain your answer.
   c) What will happen to the speed of the car?

2 a) Explain what resultant force means.
   b) There is a force from the motor on Dodgem 3, and also a force from Dodgem 2. What will the resultant force do to Dodgem 3?

We use this formula to calculate speed:

mean (average) speed = distance travelled ÷ time taken (or s = d/t)

This formula can be written out as a triangle.

d = distance travelled
s = mean speed
t = time taken

90

Speed can be measured in metres per second (m/s), kilometres per hour (km/h) or miles per hour (mph).

 The fastest speed a bicycle has achieved is 167 mph. Fred Rompelberg from Holland did this in 1995 on the Bonneville Salt Flats in Utah in the USA.

 3 Jack can run 5 km in half an hour. What is his mean speed in km/h?

 Design an investigation to work out the speed of toy cars down a ramp.
- Does the height of the ramp or the kind of surface make a difference to the speed of the cars?

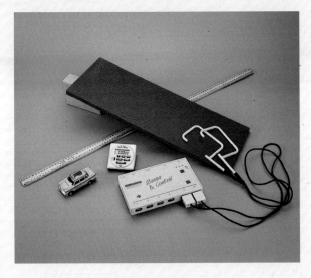

 4 a) What causes friction?
   b) Write down two things that friction can do.

5 Give two examples of useful friction.

6 Why are worn tyres dangerous when driving in wet conditions?

Speed is affected by **friction**. Friction occurs when different surfaces are in contact. If the two surfaces are rough then they cannot slide easily across each other. When two rough surfaces rub together heat is produced and the surfaces quickly wear down.

A puck easily slides across an icy surface because both surfaces are smooth.

Friction can be useful. Car tyres stop the car from slipping on the road. Wet or icy surfaces reduce friction. Car tyres are specially designed with grooves which push water away in wet weather. This increases friction and makes the tyres safer on wet roads. However, tyres wear out and have to be replaced every few years.

Racing cars have large tyres to increase the surface in contact with the race track and increase friction. This stops them spinning off the track.

You should know...

- **The formula for speed.**
- **The units for speed.**
- **Unbalanced forces can produce a change in direction, a change in speed, or a change in shape.**
- **When forces are balanced, then an object moves at a steady speed or remains stationary.**

How can you work out the pressure on something?

Pressure is the amount of *force* pushing on a certain *area*. The size of the pressure depends on the size of the force, and the size of the area it is pushing on. High pressures will cut or break things more easily than low pressures.

If you keep the size of the force the same:
- for a large area the pressure will be low
- for a small area the pressure will be high.

Force is measured in newtons, and the area in square metres. The pressure is measured in newtons per square metre (N/m^2). This unit is also called a **pascal** (Pa). 1 Pa = 1 N/m^2.

This vehicle has large caterpillar tracks which spread its weight over a big area. The large area of the tracks makes the pressure smaller so the vehicle does not sink in the mud. Look at the size of the people.

We use this formula to calculate pressure. It can be written out as a triangle.

$$pressure = \frac{force}{area}$$

f = force
p = pressure
a = area

A football boot has studs. The small area of the studs puts more pressure on the ground. The high pressure makes the studs sink in so they give a better grip.

1 Why is it an advantage to have caterpillar tracks on some vehicles?

2 Explain why a camel has large feet.

3 Why is it easier to cut things with a sharp knife than with a blunt knife?

If the area being measured is small you can measure it in square centimetres (cm^2). The unit of pressure will then be N/cm^2.

area of shoes 150 cm^2 area of boots 360 cm^2

To work out how much pressure is put on the ground by the woman in shoes:

$$\text{pressure} = \frac{\text{force}}{\text{area}}$$

$$= \frac{600\,\text{N}}{150\,\text{cm}^2}$$

$$= 4\,\text{N/cm}^2$$

P Compare the highest and lowest pressure that your weight will put on different parts of your body.
You need to:
- weigh yourself in newtons
- measure the area of a part of the body you can balance on (eg head, feet, tiptoes, hands).

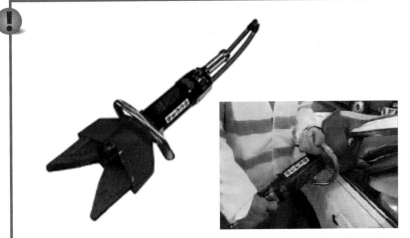

Cars often have reinforcement to protect the driver and passengers if there is an accident. Firemen sometimes need to cut people out of cars after a crash. This new 'super cutter' delivers a pressure of about 500 million N/m^2 at the jaws. The cutter can even cut through the extra reinforcement that expensive cars have for safety.

4 How much pressure is put on the ground by the woman's boots?

5 A hippopotamus has a mass of 4 tonnes (4000 kg). His four feet cover an area of 0.08 m^2 in total.
  a) What does the hippo weigh? (Remember 1 kg has a weight of 10 N.)
  b) What is his pressure on the ground?

6 Copy and complete the sentences. Pressure is measured in ____ or ____. It is calculated using the equation: pressure equals ____ divided by ____. A force of 15 N acting on an area of 3 cm^2 causes a pressure of ____ N/cm^2. If you reduce the area, the pressure becomes ____.

You should know...

- Pressure depends on the size of the force and the area it is pushing on.

- Pressure is measured in pascals (Pa), newtons per square metre (N/m^2) or newtons per square centimetre (N/cm^2).

- 1 Pa = 1 N/m^2.

How do liquids and gases exert pressure?

Particles in a gas.

Everything is made up of tiny particles. In liquids and gases, the particles are moving around in all directions. As they move they bump into each other and any surfaces they come into contact with. The force of the particles hitting things causes pressure. Pressure in liquids and gases comes from all directions.

When you pump up a bicycle tyre you put more air inside it. The particles in a gas are a long way apart and so they can be squashed closer together. When a gas is squashed we say that it is **compressed**. The pressure in a compressed gas is higher because there are more particles and so more particles hit the wall of the tyre each second.

*The pressure in water increases with depth. The ship stays afloat because the water pressure is pressing on the hull creating a force called **upthrust**. This balances the weight of the ship pushing down.*

*Tyres with air inside are called **pneumatic** tyres (from the Greek word for air). When a tyre is squashed the air pressure inside gets higher, so the tyre tries to spring back.*

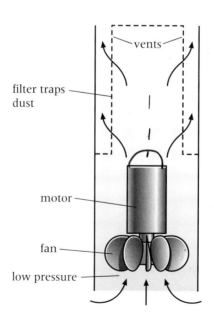

This diagram shows a vacuum cleaner. The fan inside the cleaner blows air out of the vents. This reduces the air pressure inside it. The higher air pressure outside then pushes air into the cleaner, carrying dust and dirt with it.

1 a) What is a pneumatic tyre?
   b) Give two examples of vehicles which have pneumatic tyres.

2 Why does a vacuum cleaner 'suck up' dust?

3 Look at the picture. Why does this hook stay fixed to the wall?

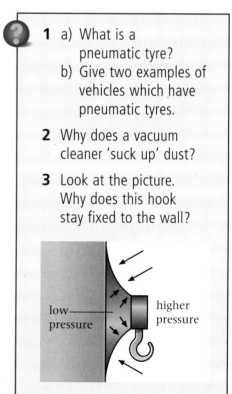

In 1654 in Magdeburg, Germany, Otto van Guericke demonstrated the enormous effect of air pressure. He had two large metal bowls made, which he placed together and pumped the air out. Two teams of horses were attached to the bowls and they were unable to pull them apart. Once the air was allowed back in the bowls came apart easily.

You may have used a pressurised container before you came to school today. Aerosol products include air fresheners, deodorants and body sprays. There are over 2000 different aerosol products on the market today.

An aerosol can is an air tight, pressurised container. Pressing the button on top opens a valve. The product is pushed out because the pressure inside the can is higher than the pressure outside.

 Aerosols were invented in Norway in 1929, but became more widespread after the Second World War. During the war, large aerosols called 'bug bombs' were used by soldiers to protect against disease-carrying insects. These diseases caused more deaths than the bullets did.

4 a) What is an aerosol?
  b) How does it work?

5 Why were aerosols used in World War II?

6 Name three aerosols found in your home.

You should know...

● Pressure is the force acting on a certain area.

● Gases can be put under pressure.

● What a pneumatic tyre is and why it works.

● What an aerosol is and how it works.

What are hydraulic systems?

Liquids cannot be compressed because there are no gaps between the particles. Since they cannot be compressed, liquids can be used to send forces from one place to another. A system which uses liquids like this is called a **hydraulic** system. Brakes in a car operate using a hydraulic system.

 1 Why can't a liquid be compressed?

2 What is a hydraulic system?

Hydraulic systems can be used to increase the size of a force. Look carefully at the diagram below.

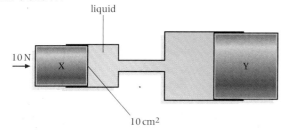

X puts a pressure on the liquid.

$$\text{pressure} = \frac{\text{force}}{\text{area}}$$

$$= \frac{10\,\text{N}}{10\,\text{cm}^2}$$

$$= 1\,\text{N/cm}^2$$

 3 Why does the force at Y only move half the original distance? (Hint: think about the amount of liquid).

4 What would the force at Y be if the area was 30 cm²?

5 a) What would the force at Y be if the area was 5 cm²?
b) How far would the force at Y move?

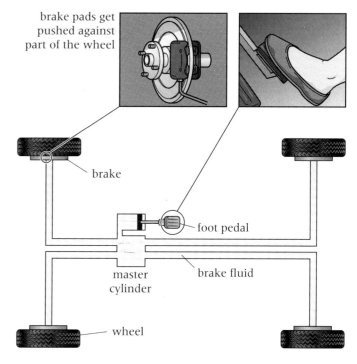

brake pads get pushed against part of the wheel

brake

foot pedal

master cylinder

brake fluid

wheel

The braking system in a car.

The area of Y is 20 cm². We can rearrange the pressure equation to let us calculate the force at Y.

Force = pressure × area
= 1 N/cm² × 20 cm²

Force at Y = 20 N.

We have not got something for nothing. The large force at Y only moves half of the distance, so the energy we get out is the same as the energy we put in.

You should know...
● **Liquids cannot be compressed.**
● **Hydraulic systems can transmit forces and increase them.**

How can water pressure affect our bodies?

The pressure in water increases as you go deeper, as there is more weight of water above you.

When we are on land, the pressure inside our bodies is equal to the pressure outside our bodies. As divers go deeper into the sea, the pressure outside their bodies increases but the pressure inside does not. Their lungs contract.

If divers stay under water for a long time some of the high pressure gas they are breathing dissolves in their blood. If they try to come to the surface too quickly the dissolved gases can form bubbles in their blood. The bubbles increase in size as the water pressure decreases, and can stop the flow of blood. This condition is called the **bends**, or **decompression sickness**, and can be fatal.

The Paumotan pearl divers of the central Tuamotu Archipelago in French Polynesia are incredible divers. They dive with no air supply, but they can descend to depths of more than 40 metres and work for up to two minutes.

A decompression chamber helps the pressure in the body of a diver return to normal very slowly.

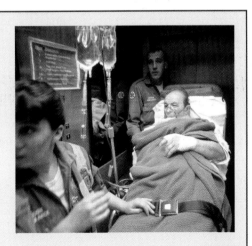

1. Why do your ears hurt if you swim underwater at the deep end of the pool?

2. Why do Paumotan divers' lungs contract when they dive for pearls?

3. What causes the bends?

4. Look at the picture on the right. Why do the bottles have to be held above the patient?

5. a) Air pressure decreases as you climb up a mountain. Explain why this happens.
   b) Find out what altitude sickness is, its causes and symptoms, and how it can be avoided.

How can you increase the size of a force?

Levers are simple **machines**. They can make work easier by increasing the size of a force.

Forces can move objects by turning them around a **pivot** or **fulcrum**. A seesaw is a lever. When you push down on one side you are applying an **effort** and the person on the other side, the **load**, moves up. The downward force of the **effort** on one side causes the **load** on the other side to move up.

A longer lever makes lifting the load easier.

force from load   effort

We use many simple levers in the home. Most levers work by changing a small force into a larger one. The lever acts as a **force multiplier**.

?
1 What is a lever?

2 Give another name for the pivot and explain what it is.

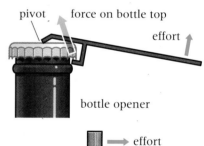

pivot   force on bottle top

effort

bottle opener

?
3 Why is a door handle on the opposite edge to the hinges?

4 Copy the drawing, and show how you would use a spoon handle to open the tin. Label the effort, pivot and force on lid.

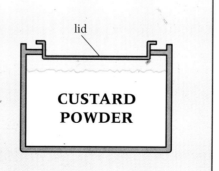

lid

CUSTARD POWDER

effort

force on nail

pivot

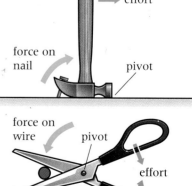

force on wire   pivot

effort

Simple levers used at home.

How does the length of a lever affect the force you need to lift a load?
- How will you measure the effort and load?
- Does it matter where the pivot is?

Arms can also act as levers. In the photograph the elbow is acting as a pivot. The **biceps muscle** uses the **radius bone** as a lever.

Muscles can pull by **contracting**, but they cannot push. You bend your arm up by contracting the biceps muscle, but you need another muscle to straighten it again. All joints need at least two muscles which act in opposite directions to one another. These are called **antagonistic** pairs of muscles. The opposing muscle to the biceps is the **triceps**.

 In the year 2000 the man with the largest biceps was Dennis Sester of the USA. His biceps each measured over 76 cm in girth. He began to build them up as a teenager wrestling with pigs on his parents' farm.

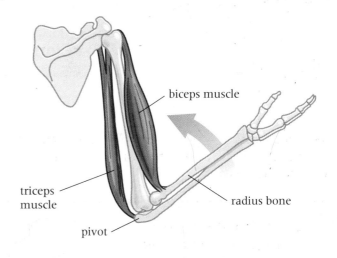

biceps muscle

triceps muscle

pivot

radius bone

5 Explain how your hand can lift a weight using the elbow as a pivot. Use the words load and effort in your answer.

6 When you stand on tiptoes you are also using bones as levers. Where do you think the pivot is?

You should know...
- How simple levers work.
- Some examples of uses of levers.
- Some examples of levers in the body.
- How pairs of antagonistic muscles move joints.

Where do we find rotating forces?

A lever can be used to apply a force which turns something around a pivot. This is called the **turning effect** or **moment** of the force.

 1 List three turning effects in the pictures on the right.

2 What is another name for the turning effect of a force?

The size of the moment depends on the size of the force, and the distance between the force and the pivot. Moments are measured in units called **newton meters (N m)**.

We use this formula to calculate moments:

$$\text{moment of the force (N m)} = \text{force (N)} \times \text{perpendicular distance from the pivot (m)}$$

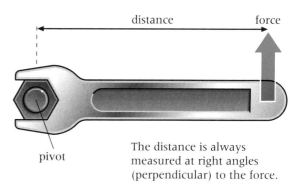

The distance is always measured at right angles (perpendicular) to the force.

The woman in this picture is tightening a nut with a wrench. She is holding it 30 cm from the nut and putting a 10 N force on it.

Distance from the pivot = 30 cm = 0.3 m

Moment = force × distance
= 10 N × 0.3 m
= 3 N m

P How many different ways can you arrange the masses to balance?
- Can you work out a rule for making them balance?

 3 A mechanic applies a force of 50 N at a distance of 40 cm from the pivot on a wheel wrench. What is the size of the moment?

4 A plumber uses a spanner on a tap. He puts a force of 100 N on the spanner 15 cm from the tap. What is the size of the moment?

When an object is balanced, the clockwise and anticlockwise moments are the same. The object is in **equilibrium**.

In the seesaw below the small girl is balancing the larger boy.

This is because:
the anticlockwise moment = the clockwise moment.

This is known as **the principle of moments.**

This crane shows the principle of moments in use. The jib acts as a lever pivoted at the tower. The sliding pulley block changes the load the crane can lift.

anti-clockwise movement   clockwise movement

The girl weighs less than the boy. However, she is able to balance the boy because she is further away from the pivot.

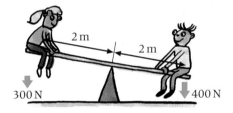

300 N   400 N

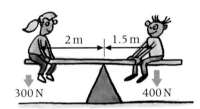

2 m   1.5 m

300 N   400 N

This seesaw is not balanced. The boy needs to move nearer to the pivot.

This seesaw is balanced. The weight multiplied by the distance from the pivot on each side is equal.

This is the largest tower crane in the world. It is 120 metres high and lifts loads up to 100 tonnes (1 million newtons).

5 What is the principle of moments?

6 Give two examples of the principle of moments in use.

7 a) Calculate the clockwise and anticlockwise turning moments on this crane.

   b) If the distance of the left-hand load is reduced to 20 m from the tower, what is the maximum load that can be lifted?

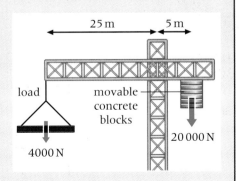

25 m   5 m

load   movable concrete blocks

4000 N   20 000 N

You should know...

● **What the turning effect or moment of a force is.**

● **The turning effect depends upon the size of the force, and the distance of the force from the pivot.**

● **The principle of moments.**

What is the difference between heat and temperature?

Heat and **temperature** are related but are not the same. We can measure temperature with a thermometer but we cannot measure the amount of heat something contains with one. This may sound strange but:

- Temperature describes how hot or cold an object is and it is usually measured in **degrees Celsius (°C)**.
- Heat is a form of energy and, like all energy, is measured in **joules (J)**. Another name for heat energy is **thermal** energy.

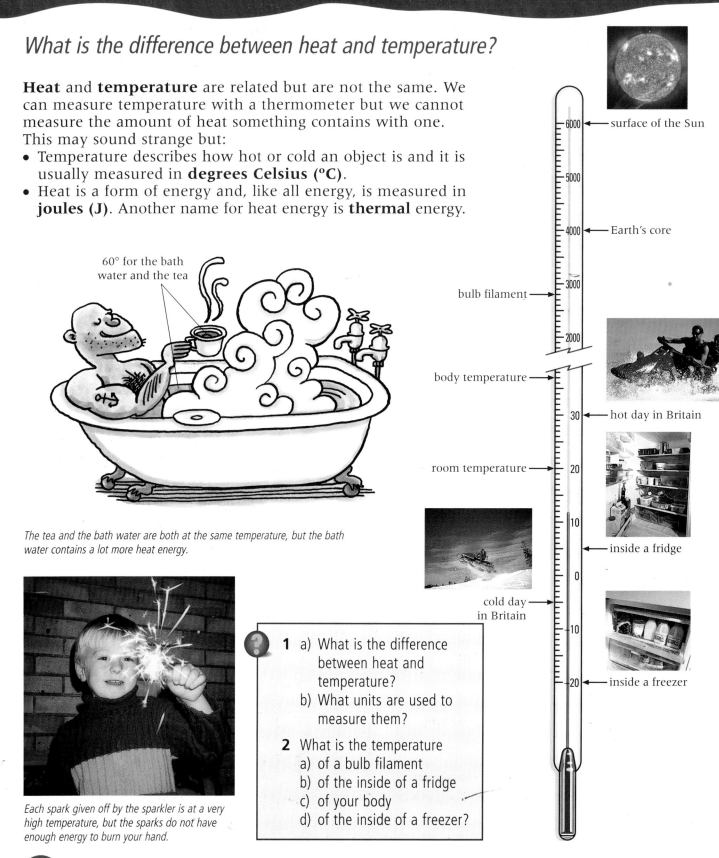

60° for the bath water and the tea

The tea and the bath water are both at the same temperature, but the bath water contains a lot more heat energy.

Each spark given off by the sparkler is at a very high temperature, but the sparks do not have enough energy to burn your hand.

— surface of the Sun — 6000

— 5000

— Earth's core — 4000

bulb filament → 3000

— 2000

body temperature →

hot day in Britain → 30

room temperature → 20

— 10

inside a fridge →

— 0

cold day → in Britain

inside a freezer → 20

— 10

— 20 → inside a freezer

? **1** a) What is the difference between heat and temperature?
   b) What units are used to measure them?

2 What is the temperature
   a) of a bulb filament
   b) of the inside of a fridge
   c) of your body
   d) of the inside of a freezer?

102

The highest ever temperature recorded in the shade was on 13th September 1922 at Al'Aziziyah, Libya in the Sahara Desert. It was 58 °C. The lowest temperature recorded was −89.2 °C in Antarctica during July 1983.

hot water   warm water   iced water

Is our skin a reliable way to tell how hot something is?
- Work in pairs to compare how hot you think the different bowls of water are.

It takes two minutes to heat the water in the kettle to 60 °C. It takes over an hour to heat the hot water tank to 60 °C. The hot water in the tank contains more heat energy than the water in the kettle because there is a lot more water.

3 a) Where is the hottest place on Earth?
b) Where is the coldest place on Earth?

The amount of heat energy in something depends on three things:
- its temperature
- the material it is made from
- its mass.

Heat energy always flows from a hot object to a cool one. The cool object becomes hotter and the hot object becomes cooler until they are both at the same temperature.

4 Why does a bath full of hot water contain a lot more heat energy than a cup of tea at the same temperature?

5 Why don't you get burned by the sparks from a sparkler?

6 a) What happens to the temperature of a drink when you put an ice cube into it?
b) What happens to the temperature of the ice cube?
c) What will happen to the temperature of the drink if you leave it standing for a whole day?

You should know...
- **The difference between temperature and heat.**
- **Thermal energy is another name for heat energy.**
- **Some examples of common temperatures.**

What happens when the temperature changes?

The **particle model** of matter is a way of explaining the properties of materials. It says that everything is made of particles, and the particles are moving all the time. In solids the particles vibrate around fixed positions, but in liquids and gases the particles can move around and go past each other. The scientific name for movement energy is kinetic energy, so these ideas are sometimes called the **kinetic theory**. The kinetic theory can help us to explain why substances **expand** (get bigger) when they are heated and **contract** (get smaller) when they are cooled.

1 Describe how particles move in solids, liquids and gases.

2 What do the words expand and contract mean?

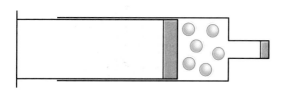

When liquids or gases are heated, the particles move around faster, and need more space to move in. The liquid or gas expands.

When a substance is heated, the particles get more energy. The heat energy is transferred to kinetic energy in the particles, and they start to move faster.

When a solid is heated, the particles in the solid vibrate more, and need more space to move in. The solid expands.

3 What happens to the movement of particles when a substance is heated?

4 Why do you think that solids contract when they cool down?

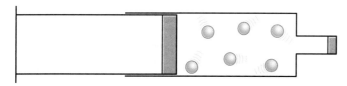

5 Why are bubbles of air coming out of the flask in the drawing on the right?

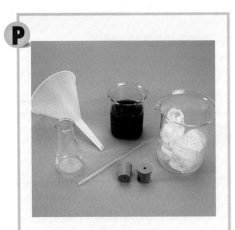

P

How can you use ideas about expanding liquids to make a thermometer?
- How will you know which temperatures it is showing?
- Explain how it works.

Most substances expand when they are heated and contract when they are cooled. However, water expands when its temperature drops below 4°C. This means that a lump of ice has a greater volume than the liquid water it was made from. Ice is less dense than water so it floats.

Gases and some liquids are kept in sealed containers. The force of the particles hitting the walls of the container causes **pressure**. If the container is heated, the substance inside it gets hotter and the particles move faster. The substance cannot expand because it is in a sealed container. The moving particles hit the walls of the container harder, and the pressure increases. If the pressure gets high enough, the container may burst.

Eggs can explode if you heat them in their shells in a microwave oven.

 7 Why do pieces of popcorn get bigger when you cook them? (Hint: think what happens to water in the corn when it is heated.)

A solid melts when the particles have enough energy to break away from their fixed positions and form a liquid. When a liquid evaporates, the particles have enough energy to escape from the liquid and form a gas.

 8 Describe what happens to the particles in steam when they cool from 150°C to −10°C.

 6 Explain why an egg will explode if you heat it too much.

Popcorn expands when it is cooked.

You should know...

- Solids, liquids and gases are made from moving particles.
- Particles move faster when a substance is heated, and the substance expands.
- Substances contract when they cool down.
- The particle model of matter is also called the kinetic theory.

How can temperatures be measured?

To measure temperature you need a thermometer or a temperature sensor. The tables show some of the different types of thermometers and temperature sensors available today.

Thermometer
Mercury in glass   Range: −39 °C to 630 °C   Advantages: accurate, mercury expands easily and is easy to see.   Disadvantages: expensive, dangerous if broken. 
Alcohol in glass   Range: −117 °C to 79 °C   Advantages: cheap, can be used in very cold areas.   Disadvantages: may not be accurate, sticks to glass. 

Sensor
Thermistor   This is a resistor and the resistance varies with temperature. It is used as part of an electric circuit.   Range: depends on the type.   Advantages: can give continuous readings, provides an electrical signal which can be used by computer equipment.   Disadvantages: may have limited range, not very accurate. 
Thermocouple   Two metals joined in a circuit can generate a small voltage when there is a difference of temperature.   Range: depends on metals used.   Advantages: cheap, gives continuous readings, can measure the temperature of very small objects.   Disadvantages: not always very accurate. 
Liquid crystal   Some crystals change colour when their temperature changes.   Range: depends on the types of liquid crystal used.   Advantages: cheap, easy to read.   Disadvantages: not very accurate 

Liquid crystals were discovered in 1888 by Austrian botanist Friedrich Reinitzer. He noticed that cholesteryl benzoate was neither completely solid nor completely liquid in a certain temperature range. He concluded that a new state of matter had been discovered and called it the liquid crystal phase.

1 Explain which thermometer or sensor you would use in:
   a) a fridge
   b) a thermostat.

2 If you had to take your own temperature, which type of thermometer would you place:
   a) under your tongue
   b) on your forehead?

3 A bimetallic strip can be used as a temperature sensor.
   a) Find out what a bimetallic strip is, and what happens to it when it gets hot. Explain your answer in terms of particles.
   b) Give two examples of where a bimetallic strip could be used.

The Kelvin scale

What is the Kelvin temperature scale?

The hotter something gets, the faster its particles move. The temperature of a substance depends on the mean speed of its particles.

Temperature is measured with a thermometer. The scale on the thermometer is called a **temperature scale**. The **Celsius** and **Fahrenheit** scales are commonly used in the UK. Both scales are named after the scientists who first suggested them.

Celsius is the main scale used internationally, but scientists and engineers often use the **Kelvin** or **absolute scale** instead.

A weather map in degrees Celsius and Fahrenheit.

In the nineteenth century an Englishman named Lord Kelvin decided that it was inconvenient to use negative values when measuring very cold temperatures. In 1848 he proposed the Kelvin temperature scale. Like the Celsius scale, the Kelvin scale was based upon two fixed points: the freezing point of water, and the boiling point of water. However, Lord Kelvin set the zero for his scale on a different starting point. If a substance could be cooled down until all the particles stopped moving, it would be as cold as possible. The temperature would be **absolute zero**. Kelvin calculated that temperature to be −273 °C.

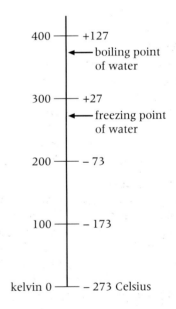

 1 What does the 'temperature' of an object tell you about the movement of the particles in it?

2 What are the two fixed points on a Celsius or Kelvin thermometer scale?

3 Why did Lord Kelvin design a new scale?

4 What is absolute zero?

5 What is the freezing point of water on the Kelvin scale?

When writing a temperature in the Kelvin scale it is usual to leave out the ° symbol and just use the letter K. The boiling point of water is 100 °C or 373 K.

107

How is heat energy transferred through solids?

Metals are good **conductors** of heat, but substances like wool, water or air are not. The particle model of matter can help to explain why some substances let heat flow through them easily, and some do not.

When a solid is heated, the particles in it gain energy and vibrate more. The particles bump into each other, and pass the energy on. We say that the solid **conducts** heat. Conduction happens best in solids, because the particles are very close together. Conduction does not take place very well in liquids, and hardly at all in gases.

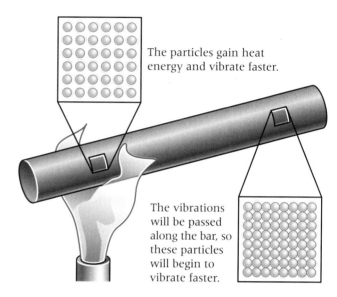

The particles gain heat energy and vibrate faster.

The vibrations will be passed along the bar, so these particles will begin to vibrate faster.

If the bar is heated at one end the particles vibrate faster. Their extra movements are passed along the bar and conduction takes place.

Some materials are better conductors of heat than others. Metals are the best conductors of heat. Metals conduct electricity because the **electrons** in them can move around. When the solid is heated, the electrons move faster. They bump into the atoms in the metal, and make them vibrate. The electrons help to pass on heat energy.

Solids that are mainly made of non-metals, or have little pockets of trapped air, do not conduct heat very well. They are **insulators**.

> **1** a) Name one material that is a good conductor of heat.
> b) Name three materials that do not conduct heat well.
>
> **2** Explain how heat is conducted through a solid object. Use ideas about particles in your answer.

> **3** Why are metals good conductors of heat?
> **4** Why are some materials good insulators?
> **5** Why is carpet a good insulator?

call 4 sex ←No way!

☎ 01908 225047

You can tell whether something is a conductor or an insulator by touching it. If you walk around in your bare feet, tiles feel colder than carpets. This is because the tiles are a better conductor of heat than the carpet. The heat is conducted quickly away from you by the tiles, so your feet feel cold.

Glass is a poor conductor of heat. If you pour very hot water into a thick walled glass it may break. This is because the inside heats up a moment before the outside, so the inside expands before the outside.

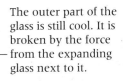

The outer part of the glass is still cool. It is broken by the force from the expanding glass next to it.

This part of the glass heats up and expands.

6 Why does a plastic fizzy drink bottle usually *feel* warmer than a metal can of drink, even if they are both at the same temperature?

7 Why does thick glass break more easily than thin glass if part of it is heated?

8 Find out what forms of insulation animals have.

P Which material is the most effective lagging for water pipes?
- How can you test different materials?
- How can you make sure your test is fair?

Animals' fur keeps them warm because it traps air between the hairs and acts as an insulator. Polar bears' fur is an even better insulator, because it is made of hollow tubes so that even more air is trapped.

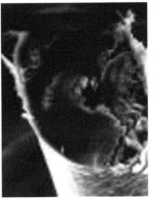

You should know...

- When heat energy passes through a solid, conduction takes place.
- Metals are good conductors.
- Insulators often contain pockets of trapped air.
- How conduction can be explained using the particle model.

Call for a walk:

1410800   116 118

How does heat travel through liquids and gases?

Heat does not travel through liquids and gases very well by conduction, but it can travel by **convection**. The particles in liquids and gases can move around. Liquids and gases are all **fluids**.

When a fluid is heated, the particles move around faster. The fluid expands and it becomes less dense because the same amount of mass is taking up more space. If only part of the fluid is being heated, that part becomes less dense than the cooler fluid around it, and it starts to rise. Cooler fluid moves in to take its place, and a **convection current** forms.

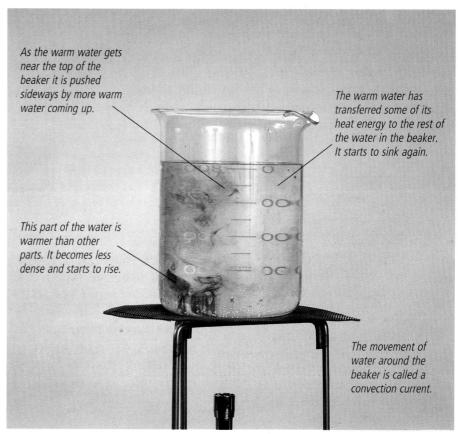

As the warm water gets near the top of the beaker it is pushed sideways by more warm water coming up.

The warm water has transferred some of its heat energy to the rest of the water in the beaker. It starts to sink again.

This part of the water is warmer than other parts. It becomes less dense and starts to rise.

The movement of water around the beaker is called a convection current.

A purple dye can be used to show a convection current.

1 a) What is a fluid?
   b) Write down three examples of fluids.

2 What happens to the density of a fluid when it is heated?

Most rooms in the home are heated by convection. The radiator heats the air around it, and the hot air rises to the ceiling. The colder air near the ceiling is pushed away, and sinks. A convection current is created.

Convection currents can also form when part of a fluid is colder than its surroundings. An ice lolly will absorb heat energy from the air around it, and the air will cool down. The cold air will become denser than the surrounding air, and sink.

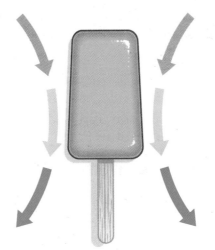

Convection plays a large part in the weather. Some parts of the Earth are warmed more than others by energy from the Sun. Warm spots on the Earth heat the air above them, and the hot air rises. The rising air can form convection currents which we feel as wind. Water vapour in the rising air can form clouds. Rain falls when there is too much water vapour in the air or when clouds are blown over mountains.

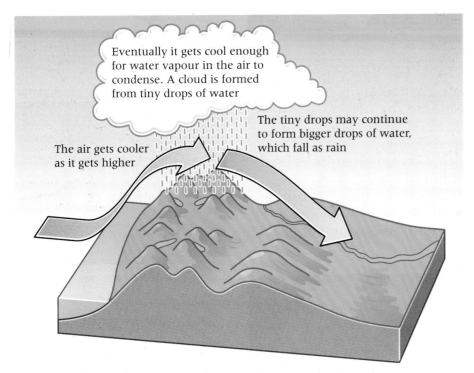

Eventually it gets cool enough for water vapour in the air to condense. A cloud is formed from tiny drops of water

The tiny drops may continue to form bigger drops of water, which fall as rain

The air gets cooler as it gets higher

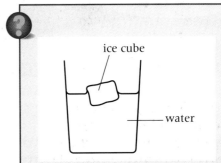

3 a) Copy this diagram, and add arrows to show the direction of the convection current caused by the ice cube.
b) Explain why the convection current forms.

Some birds use rising columns of warm air to keep them in the air. The highest altitude recorded for a bird was when a Ruppell's vulture hit an airliner at 11 300 m (11.3 km)!

4 How can convection currents cause rain?

5 Use ideas about particles and convection to explain how a hot air balloon flies.

You should know...

- Liquids and gases are called fluids.
- Heat is mainly transferred through fluids by convection.
- Convection currents can be formed by hot or cold objects.
- Some examples of convection currents.

How does heat travel from the Sun to the Earth?

There is nothing but empty space between the Sun and the Earth, so heat cannot travel from the Sun to the Earth by conduction or convection. All the heat we get from the Sun travels as **radiation** (sometimes called **infrared radiation**).

Infrared radiation travels as waves, like light waves. It does not need anything (a **medium**) to travel through, and it can also go through transparent substances like air or glass.

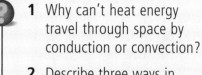

1 Why can't heat energy travel through space by conduction or convection?

2 Describe three ways in which infrared radiation and light waves are similar.

The heat from the flame radiates in all directions.

Infrared radiation can be focused using a magnifying glass.

The shiny surface at the back of the heater reflects infrared radiation into the room.

All hot things give out or **emit** infrared radiation. When radiation hits something, it is taken into the object, or **absorbed**.

Thermal imagers are instruments that create pictures of heat rather than light. They measure infrared energy and convert the data into maps of temperatures. Thermal imaging can be used for filming things at night, and for finding the temperature of remote parts of the Earth by taking photos from space.

The police use infrared cameras to help catch criminals.

3 What is a thermal image?

4 Give two examples of the use of a thermal imager.

5 Design a table to show how heat can travel through transparent and opaque solids, liquids and gases.

This image shows how much waste heat is being emitted on Earth.

You should know...

● Heat can travel as infrared radiation.

● Infrared radiation does not need a medium to travel through.

Which colours absorb radiation the best?

All hot things **emit** infrared radiation. When radiation hits something, it can be **absorbed** by the object. Some surfaces emit or absorb more infrared radiation than others.

After a marathon the runners are very hot, and their bodies are radiating infrared energy. If they cool down too quickly they may become chilled, so they are wrapped with silvery sheets. Shiny surfaces reflect the heat back to the body.

Shiny, silvery surfaces are the worst absorbers, as they reflect most of the radiation. Dull black surfaces are the best absorbers.

Surfaces which are good absorbers are also good emitters. Silvery surfaces are the worst emitters and dull black surfaces are the best emitters.

P Why does the fire fighter wear a shiny safety suit? How could you investigate whether the colour or shininess of the suit makes the most difference?

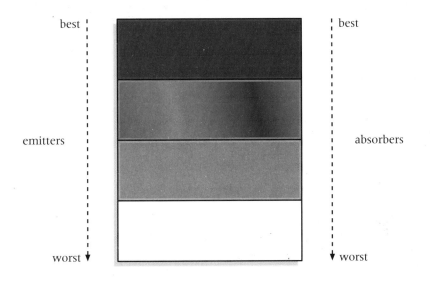

best — emitters — worst

best — absorbers — worst

?

1 You have a black cup and a white cup. Which would you use if you wanted to keep your coffee hot longest? Explain your answer.

2 Why are the houses in southern Spain often painted white?

3 You can use a lens to focus sunlight onto a newspaper. Which will burn more easily, the print or the white paper? Explain your answer.

4 Explain how spreading soot onto snow could help it to melt faster.

5 Most people have radiators in their houses painted white. Is this the best colour for a radiator? Explain your answer.

What is beyond the Earth?

The **solar system** is made up of the Sun and the nine **planets** moving in elliptical **orbits** around it. There are also a lot of asteroids (small lumps of rock). The Moon orbits the Earth. Most of the other planets have moons of their own. The Sun's **gravity** keeps the planets in their orbits.

Asteroids

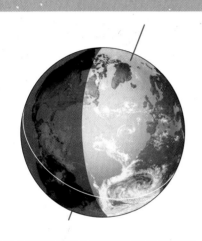

The Earth's axis is tilted, so we have seasons. When it is summer in Britain, the North Pole is tilted towards the Sun. Days are longer in the summer, and they are hotter because the Sun is higher in the sky and its rays are more concentrated. When it is summer in the northern hemisphere, it is winter in the southern hemisphere.

Mars

Earth

Venus

Mercury

Sun

Mercury, Venus, Earth, Mars and Pluto are rocky planets.

The Sun is a **star**. Stars make their own light and heat. Millions of stars form a **galaxy**. The stars in a galaxy are held together by the force of gravity between them. There are millions of galaxies in the **Universe**.

Not to scale.

The temperature of a planet depends on its distance from the Sun. Pluto is the coldest planet, because it is furthest from the Sun.

Pluto

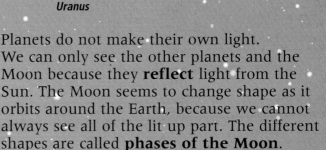

Neptune

Jupiter, Saturn, Uranus and Neptune are made mainly of gas.

Uranus

Planets do not make their own light. We can only see the other planets and the Moon because they **reflect** light from the Sun. The Moon seems to change shape as it orbits around the Earth, because we cannot always see all of the lit up part. The different shapes are called **phases of the Moon**.

Saturn

Jupiter

Artificial satellites can be used to observe the Earth, and to look at the planets and stars. Satellites can also be used to transmit TV pictures and telephone calls.

1 What is the difference between a star and a planet?

2 a) What is the solar system?
   b) How does the temperature of a planet depend on its distance from the Sun?

3 a) What are asteroids?
   b) Where are they found?

4 a) What keeps the planets in orbit around the Sun?
   b) What keeps the Moon in orbit around the Earth?

5 Why does the Moon have phases?

6 a) Why does the Earth have seasons?
   b) Why is the weather warmer in the summer?
   c) Why are the days longer in summer than in winter? Draw a diagram to help you explain.

What are the forces on a spacecraft?

There are lots of different forces on a spacecraft during its journey into space.

When the Space Shuttle is on the launch pad, **gravity** is pulling it downwards. The force of gravity on the Shuttle is its **weight**. The ground is also pushing up on it (**upthrust**). The two forces are **balanced**, so nothing happens.

When the Shuttle's engines start, there is an upwards force from the engines. When the force from the engines is bigger than the force of gravity, the Shuttle will start to move. The forces are **unbalanced**, and the Shuttle **changes speed**.

When the Shuttle is in orbit, it does not need to use its engines. It keeps moving at the same speed around the Earth. There is nothing to slow it down, because there is no air in space to cause **air resistance**.

Mass is the amount of matter in something, and is measured in **kilograms (kg)**. **Weight** is the force of gravity on something, and is measured in **newtons (N)**. The weight of an object depends on where it is; the mass of an object does not change.

upwards force from ground

weight

force from engines

weight

Unbalanced forces can make something start or stop moving, change its speed or its direction of movement, or change its shape.

Air resistance is a kind of **friction**. Friction happens when two things rub together. Water resistance is also a form of friction. Friction slows things down, produces heat energy, and wears things away.

When the Shuttle is in orbit gravity is still pulling on it. Gravity is a **non-contact force**. It can pull on the Shuttle even when the Shuttle is not touching the Earth. The force of gravity makes the Shuttle change direction.

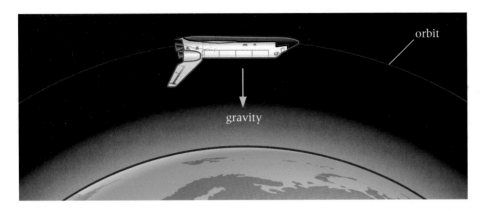

When the Shuttle has finished its mission, it has to come back to Earth. When it enters the atmosphere, friction between the Shuttle and the air makes it heat up. The underside of the Shuttle is covered in a special heat resistant material to protect it. When it comes in to land, its wings produce an upwards force (lift) that helps to balance the downwards force of gravity. When it is on the runway, it uses a parachute to increase air resistance, and this helps to slow it down.

1 What can unbalanced forces do?

2 What happens to the speed of something when the forces on it are balanced?

3 a) Name the three non-contact forces.
   b) Name three contact forces.

4 What three things can friction do to a moving object?

5 The Shuttle does not need to use its engines in space to keep moving. Why not?

6 a) Draw a sketch of the Shuttle just before it lands. Show the forces on it using arrows. Label the forces.
   b) Draw another sketch of the Shuttle when it is slowing down on the runway. Show the forces on it.

7 The mass of an astronaut is 60 kg. She weighs 600 N on the Earth. What are her mass and weight:
   a) in space, far away from any stars or planets
   b) on the Moon, where gravity is only 1/6 Earth gravity?

Where do spacecraft get their energy from?

Everything that happens needs **energy**. A lot of energy is needed to get a spacecraft into orbit. This comes from **chemical energy** stored in the fuel. When the fuel combines with oxygen, **heat energy** is released. The hot gases expand and are forced out of the back of the rocket at high speed. This pushes the rocket upwards and gives it **kinetic energy**. The kinetic energy of the rocket is converted into **gravitational potential energy** as it gets higher.

> **Different kinds of energy are: heat, light, sound, electrical, kinetic, chemical, gravitational potential, strain, and nuclear.**

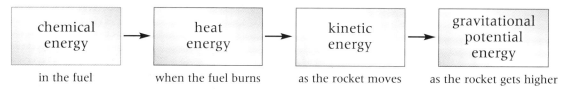

chemical energy	heat energy	kinetic energy	gravitational potential energy
in the fuel	when the fuel burns	as the rocket moves	as the rocket gets higher

This **energy flow diagram** shows the energy changes that take place when a rocket is launched into space.

A satellite or spacecraft needs energy to do the things it was put into space to do, like sending TV pictures or taking pictures of stars and planets. Most satellites need **electrical energy**, which they get from solar cells. Solar cells convert **light energy** from the Sun into electrical energy.

> **Most of the energy we use on Earth originally came from light energy from the Sun. It is converted to chemical energy in fossil fuels or food, the kinetic energy in wind and waves, or the gravitational potential energy stored in reservoirs used for hydroelectricity.
> Electricity is not an energy resource, because it has to be made using other forms of energy.**

The International Space Station uses solar cells to convert light energy into electrical energy.

Spacecraft that travel a long way from the Sun need a different source of energy. The Galileo orbiter that went to Jupiter used **nuclear energy** to produce electricity. One gram of uranium stores a million times more energy than one gram of petrol.

Energy cannot be created or destroyed, but every time energy is converted from one form to another, some of it is wasted. Wasted energy is usually heat energy. When a rocket is launched, the useful energy is kinetic energy. Heat, light and sound are also produced. These kinds of energy are wasted energy, because they are not useful for launching the rocket.

Galileo passing one of Jupiter's moons, Io.

Energy from the Sun travels through space by **radiation**. Astronauts would get very hot when they were working in space if they were not protected from the Sun. Their space suits are white to reflect energy, and they have a special cooling system built into their suits.

> **Heat energy can be transferred by conduction, convection, radiation and evaporation.**

---

1 Write down three kinds of stored energy.

2 Draw an energy flow diagram to show how a satellite gets electrical energy.

3 Why is it easier to use solar power in space than it is on the Earth?

4 The energy in the following energy resources originally came from the Sun. Explain how this happened for each of these resources:
a) biomass
b) coal
c) hydroelectricity
d) wind

5 a) The Galileo spacecraft could not use solar power. Why not?
b) Why does it use nuclear energy instead of using chemical energy stored in petrol?

6 Explain the difference between renewable and non-renewable energy resources, and give three examples of each.

7 a) What is conduction? Explain as fully as you can.
b) What is convection? Explain as fully as you can.
c) Why can't an astronaut in space lose heat by conduction or convection?

How do we use electricity?

Almost every machine we use needs electricity in some way. This is also true of spacecraft. The main energy that gets a rocket or the Space Shuttle into orbit comes from chemical energy stored in its fuel, but electricity is needed to control the engines, to steer the rocket, and to work communications and life-support equipment.

Electricity is a way of transferring energy. **Electrons** are given energy by a cell or generator, and move around a **circuit** made of **conducting** material. The amount of electricity that flows around a circuit depends on the **voltage** of the cell, and on the **resistance** of the circuit. A circuit with high resistance makes it difficult for electricity to flow, so the **current** is small.

There are lots of different kinds of electrical equipment on the Shuttle. The astronauts have to be able to switch them on or off separately. There are lots of different circuits in the Shuttle, and most of them are some kind of **parallel circuit**.

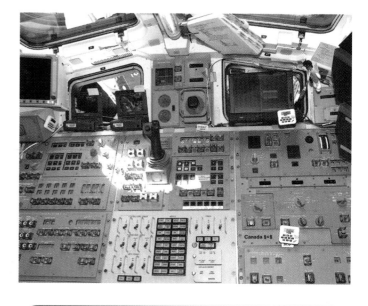

> A **current** is a flow of electrons. The units for measuring current are **amps** (A).
> The **voltage** is the amount of energy each amp of current is carrying, and is measured in **volts** (V).

> In a **series** circuit, all the components are in one loop, and they are all on or off at the same time.
> In a **parallel** circuit there are lots of different branches, and each branch can be controlled separately.

This is where astronauts prepare their food. The bags of food are tied on to stop them floating away.

Astronauts heat their food using an electric hot plate.

Electricity flowing through a coil of wire causes a **magnetic field**. **Electromagnets** can be used in **relays**, which are switches worked by electricity. Electromagnets can also be used to open or close valves that control the fuel flowing in pipes.

When the astronauts talk to the control centre on the ground, they use electricity to communicate. Microphones convert sound waves into electrical signals, and radios transmit these signals to the ground. In the control centre, electromagnets in loudspeakers convert the electrical signals back into sound.

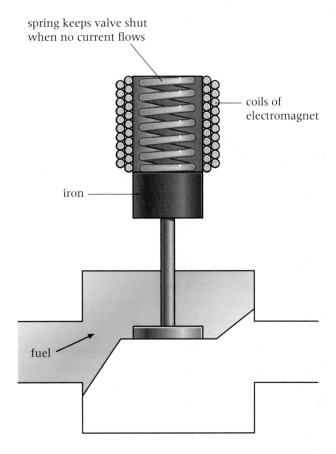

A fuel valve operated by electricity.

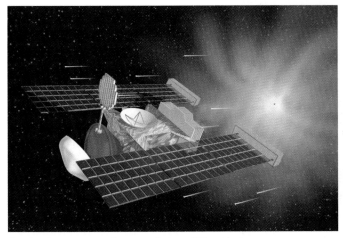

Stardust is an unmanned spacecraft that will investigate comets. Its computer and all the scientific instruments on board use electricity.

1 a) What do the words conductor and insulator mean?
   b) Give an example of a conductor and an example of an insulator.

2 a) What do you use to measure the current in a circuit?
   b) What are the units for current?

3 Explain the differences between series and parallel circuits. Give as much detail as you can.

4 Draw a diagram to show the shape of the magnetic field around a coil of wire.

5 Look at the diagram above showing a fuel valve.
   a) Is the valve open or closed in the drawing?
   b) What will happen if electricity flows in the electromagnet? Explain in as much detail as you can.

How do light and sound travel?

The launch of the Space Shuttle is very noisy. Vibrations caused by the engines travel through the air. These sound waves have a large **amplitude** so even people a long way off can hear them. People standing closer to the launch pad have to wear ear protection to stop their hearing being damaged.

> Loud sounds have a large **amplitude**; quiet sounds have a small amplitude.
> High **pitched** sounds have a short **wavelength** and high **frequency**.

The astronauts in the Space Shuttle would not be able to hear the noise from the rocket of this satellite as it is launched. There is no air in space, so sound cannot travel in space. They can see the satellite, because light can travel through space, and also through **transparent** materials like glass.

> Sound can only travel through a **medium**: a solid, liquid or gas.
> Light can travel through a **vacuum**, and also through **transparent** materials.
> Light travels much faster than sound.

Light travelling through a transparent material changes direction as it goes into and comes out of the material. This effect is called **refraction**. The windows of the Shuttle and the helmets on space suits have to be carefully designed so that refraction does not distort the view.

> **Reflection** is when light bounces off shiny surfaces like mirrors.
> **Refraction** is when light changes direction when it goes into a different material.

The helmets on space suits usually have visors that filter out some of the light from the Sun, to protect the astronauts' eyes. A filter only lets some of the light through.

> **Light is made of a mixture of different colours. If a coloured filter is used, only light of one colour can get through.**

1 a) Which materials can sound travel through?
   b) Which materials can light travel through?
   c) Which travels faster, light or sound?

2 What does a noise sound like if its wave has:
   a) a large amplitude
   b) a high frequency
   c) a long wavelength?

3 Draw a diagram of a wave, and mark the wavelength and amplitude on it.

4 Draw an accurate diagram to show a ray of light being reflected from a mirror. You will need to use a protractor.

5 Explain the difference between reflection and refraction.

6 If an astronaut had a red filter in her visor, what colour would the Space Shuttle appear to be? Explain your answer.

7 Space suits have radios in them. Explain why radios are necessary.

How can houses use less energy?

This is the INTEGER House, near Watford. It was built by the INTEGER Project to show how a house can be made energy efficient.

It does this in two ways:
- the house is well insulated, so it does not lose heat – this means that less energy is used to heat the house
- the house also has ways of using sunshine and the wind to produce heat and electricity.

The conservatory helps the house to absorb heat from the Sun.

Many of the windows are small and all of them are fitted with double glazing.
The walls are made from wood.
The earth bank on both sides of the house reduces heat losses.

Wood is a natural material and helps to insulate the house.

The living rooms open onto the conservatory.

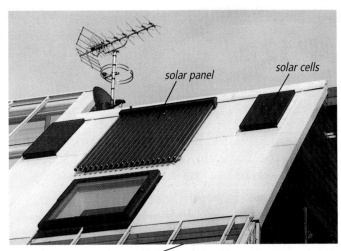

The solar cells produce electricity. The solar panel is used to help heat the water.

An automatic ventilation system and automatic blinds keep the temperature just right.

The north facing part of the roof is covered in a slow growing plant called sedum.

The INTEGER House.

A wind turbine in the garden produces a small amount of electricity.

The INTEGER House does not cost as much to heat as an ordinary house – which makes living cheaper for its owners.

It also uses less energy in the form of fossil fuels. This is important, because fossil fuels will eventually run out, and we need to make them last as long as possible. Burning fossil fuels also causes pollution in the form of acid rain, and contributes to global warming.

So, an energy efficient house has lots of benefits:
- it costs less to run
- it helps save fossil fuels
- it reduces pollution.

P The INTEGER house is well insulated to reduce the amount of heat that escapes. You could build a model of a house to investigate the insulation of a house.

- How will you make doors and windows for your house?
- How would you heat the inside of the house?
- How would you measure the temperature inside?
- How could you compare one type of insulation with another?

P The INTEGER house has a large conservatory, to help heat the house.

- How much heating does the conservatory provide?
- Does it need to be double glazed, or would double glazing stop heat energy being absorbed?
- What could you use to represent energy from the Sun?

P The outside walls of the INTEGER house are made of wood. The inside walls are filled with recycled newspaper. Part of the outside of the house is insulated by a bank of earth, and part of the roof is covered in earth, with slow growing plants on it.

- Is wood the best material for insulating the outside walls?
- How well does the earth bank insulate the house?
- Would sand work better than earth?
- How should the roof be insulated?

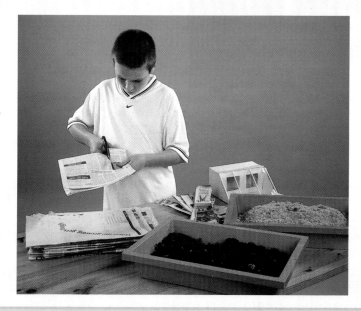

The INTEGER House does not only use insulation to save energy.

- How many other ways are there for saving energy?
- Could any of these energy saving devices be used in ordinary houses?
- How could you persuade people to use them?

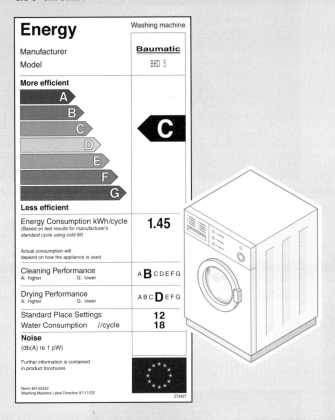

Energy	Washing machine
Manufacturer	**Baumatic**
Model	BHD 5

More efficient

A
B
C
D
E
F
G

C

Less efficient

Energy Consumption kWh/cycle *(Based on test results for manufacturer's standard cycle using cold fill)*	**1.45**
Actual consumption will depend on how the appliance is used	
Cleaning Performance A: higher G: lower	A**B**CDEFG
Drying Performance A: higher G: lower	ABC**D**EFG
Standard Place Settings	**12**
Water Consumption l/cycle	**18**
Noise (db(A) re 1 pW)	

Further information is contained in product brochures

Norm EN 50242
Washing Machine Label Directive 97/17/CE

272427

How are homes heated and insulated in other countries?

- What materials are used?
- How are houses designed to keep energy in?
- Which energy sources are used for heating?

The Inuit people can make temporary homes from ice.

The Samui people in Scandinavia live in tents in the summer when they follow the reindeer herds.

Microwaves

Using a microwave oven for cooking uses less energy than using a normal oven.

- How does a microwave oven cook food?
- How is a microwave oven different to a normal oven?
- What are microwaves, and what else are they used for?

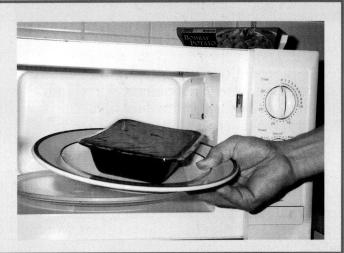

How can we use the Sun for cooking?

Energy from the Sun is often used to heat water in countries where there is a lot of sunshine. The hot water is used for washing.

In developing countries, up to 60% of families living in rural areas do not have access to safe drinking water. Millions of people die each year from diseases caused by microbes in drinking water. Water needs to be heated to about 65 °C for 6 minutes to make it safe. This process is called **pasteurisation**. Unfortunately, many people cannot heat their water because of the amount of fuel it would use.

Solar energy is used to heat water in these houses in Lesvos, Greece.

Wood is often used to provide heat energy for cooking. People have to spend a lot of time looking for wood to burn. Burning wood produces lots of smoke, which causes health problems. Using trees for fuel is one cause of deforestation, which is an increasing problem in developing countries. In cities, poor people have to spend a large proportion of their income buying fuel for cooking.

Collecting wood for cooking.

If people could use energy from the Sun for pasteurising water and cooking, they would not need to burn wood or buy fuel. They would have more time for farming, or for education. Fewer people would die from diseases passed on through drinking water, and women would be healthier because they would not have to spend as much time in smoke-filled rooms. Solar cooking could also help the environment, as fewer trees would be cut down for fuel.

How can we use the Sun for cooling?

The Sun can be a convenient source of energy in remote places. It can be used to provide electricity to run fridges, but it can also be used directly for keeping things cool!

In hot countries where people cannot afford fridges or electricity supplies, food goes bad within a few days. Farmers who grow fruit and vegetables to sell have to send someone from the family to sell food in the market every day. A Nigerian teacher, called Mohammed Bah Abba, invented a very simple way of keeping food fresh for longer.

Selling fruit in Nigeria.

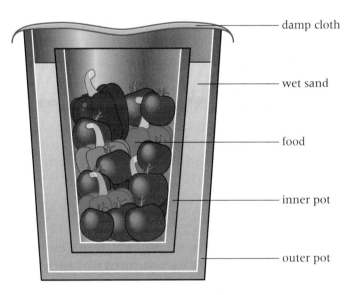

- damp cloth
- wet sand
- food
- inner pot
- outer pot

The 'pot-in-pot' system needs two earthenware pots, one inside the other. The gap between them is filled with wet sand, and the top is covered with a damp cloth. Water from the wet sand soaks through the outer pot and evaporates, keeping the pots cool. As long as the sand and the cloth are kept wet, food inside the inner pot stays much cooler than the outside air.

Food kept in the pot will stay fresh for over three weeks. Children do not have to be sent to sell food every day, so they can go to school.

Mohammed Bah Abba with his 'pot-in-pot'.

Solar cooker

Britain does not have as much Sun as some countries, but you can still use energy from the Sun for cooking. Design and build a solar cooker.

- What materials will you need?
- Where will you put it?
- What foods could you cook in it?

Camp cooler

The 'pot-in-pot' system for keeping food cool is very simple, but heavy to carry. Can you adapt the design to make a food cooler for backpackers?

- What materials could you use to make your containers?
- What will go between the two layers?
- How heavy will your design be to carry?
- How can you test it to see how well it works?

Elephants' ears

Why do elephants have large ears? Elephants live in hot countries, and must not let their body temperatures get too high. Do their ears help them to keep cool? What else can they do to keep cool?

- What could you use as a 'model' for elephants' ears?
- How could you find out if large ears help elephants to cool down?
- Why are these elephants spraying water on themselves?

Solar survey

Your school might be able to save money by using solar energy to heat water, or you might want to try out a solar cooker. Survey your school and its grounds to decide where solar panels could be put, and to find a good location for a solar cooker.

- Which parts of the site get the most Sun all year round?
- Which parts are sheltered from the wind?
- Which parts would be the most convenient locations?

Training posters

An international aid agency wants to persuade people to use solar cookers instead of burning wood. They also want to explain how they can keep their food fresh for longer. They have workers who speak the local language, but these workers need some posters that they can show to people to help them explain. Design a set of posters for them. Your posters should explain:

- how a solar cooker works and how to set it up
- the benefits of using solar energy for cooking
- how to use pots and wet sand to keep their food cool
- the benefits of keeping food fresh.

Which cooker?

Find out about different kinds of designs, for solar cookers, their benefits and drawbacks. Design a leaflet or write an illustrated magazine article to help people chose the best. Include:

- the names of the materials used in the cooker
- how much it would cost
- whether it has to be turned to face the Sun often.

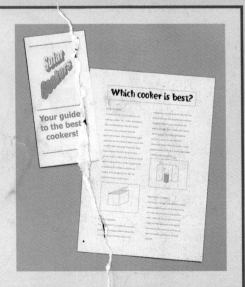

How to revise

At the end of Year 9 you will be tested on all the science you have learned over the past three years. That is a lot to learn!

Divide your time into small chunks of between 20 and 40 minutes, and take a short break (5 to 10 minutes) between each 'chunk'. You will not be able to concentrate if you try to revise for longer.

Reading through your notes or the textbook is not a very good way of learning. We can all read pages and pages of information without taking it in. Our minds are very good at day dreaming!

This way of revising doesn't work. You will need a quiet place to work, where you can sit at a table.

There are two important steps when you are revising:

1 Write down key words and short notes
Writing notes will help you to learn, but *don't* just copy out all your notes! If you think about what you are reading, and only write down important points, that will help you learn.

- If you have a list of things to learn, try repeating it over and over again. Try using mnemonics.

- You could try drawing diagrams to help you remember. Mind maps are often helpful, like this one on energy.

2 Look through your notes again.
If possible, spend 5 or 10 minutes in the evening going through the short notes, the more likely the information is to stick in your memory. Make sure you do this step, otherwise you will lose the information you have worked hard to learn.

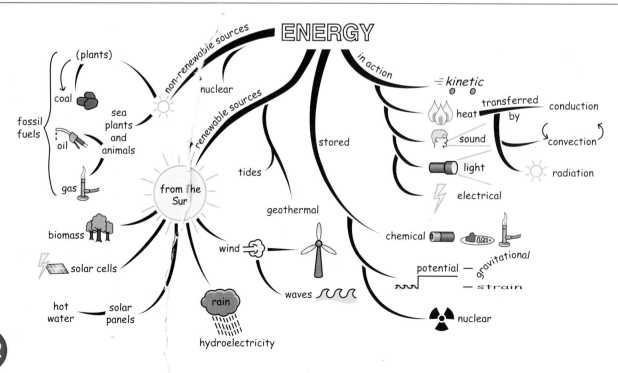

Glossary

Pronunciation note: A capital 'O' is said as in 'so'

Absorb	This means to 'soak up' or 'take in'. If something absorbs light it soaks it up and does not let it back out.
Accelerate (*axe-el-er-ate*)	To speed up or go faster.
Acid (*ass-id*)	A substance that turns litmus red. Has a pH of less than 7.
Acid rain	Rain with sulphur dioxide or nitrogen oxides dissolved in it, making it more acidic than normal.
Acne (*ack-nee*)	Spots on the skin.
Adaptations (*add-app-tay-shuns*)	The features that plants and animals have that help them live in a particular place.
Addict	Someone who feels that they need to have a certain drug is called an addict.
Addictive	A drug that is addictive makes you unable to stop taking it.
Adolescence (*add-ol-ess-sense*)	Time when both physical and emotional changes occur in humans.
Aerobic respiration	Process that releases energy from food. Needs oxygen from the air. Carbon dioxide is produced as a waste gas.
Afterbirth	When the placenta is pushed out through the vagina.
Air resistance	A force that tries to slow things down that are moving through the air. It is a type of friction.
Air sacs	Pockets in the lungs where oxygen comes out of the air and goes into the blood. Carbon dioxide is also transferred from the blood to the air in these.
Alkali (*alk-al-lie*)	A substance that turns litmus blue. Has a pH of more than 7.
Alloy	A mixture of different metals.
Aluminium	A metal used for overhead powerlines because it is light and a good electrical conductor.
Alveoli (*al-vee-O-lee*)	Small, round pockets that are grouped to form air sacs in the lungs. (Singular = alveolus.)
Amino acid (*am-mee-no ass-id*)	Proteins are digested to form amino acids.
Ammeter	Measures how much electricity is flowing around a circuit.
Amnion (*am-nee-on*)	Bag containing the amniotic fluid.
Amniotic fluid (*am-nee-ot-tick*)	Liquid surrounding the growing embryo and protecting it.
Amp (A)	The unit for current.
Amphibian (*am-fib-ee-an*)	Vertebrate with moist skin, eg a frog.
Amplitude	Half the height of a wave.
Amylase (*am-e-laze*)	An enzyme found in saliva that breaks starch down into sugar.
Anaerobic respiration	Type of respiration that does not need oxygen.
Angle of incidence (*in-sid-dense*)	The angle between the normal and the ray of light hitting a mirror.
Angle of reflection	The angle between the normal and the ray of light leaving a mirror.
Antacid (*ant-ass-id*)	A medicine containing an alkali used to cancel out some of the acid in the stomach to treat heartburn.
Antagonistic pair (*ant-tag-on-iss-tick*)	Two muscles that work a joint by pulling in opposite directions (eg biceps and triceps).
Anther	Part of the stamen. It produces pollen grains.
Antibiotics (*ant-ee-by-ot-tics*)	Substances that can kill bacteria but not viruses.
Antibodies	Chemicals made by white blood cells. They attach to microbes and help to destroy them.
Anticlockwise moment	The turning effect of a force in an anticlockwise direction around a pivot.

Anus	The opening at the end of the gut.
Appendix	Small tube branching off the large intestine. It has no function in humans.
Arachnid (*ar-ack-nid*)	Type of arthropod with four pairs of legs, eg a spider.
Armature	The iron part of a relay that moves when electricity is flowing in the solenoid.
Artery	Blood vessel that carries blood away from the heart.
Arthropod (*arth-row-pod*)	Invertebrate with jointed legs, eg a fly or spider.
Ascorbic acid	Chemical name for vitamin C.
Asexual reproduction	Producing new organisms from one parent only.
Asteroid (*ass-ter-oyd*)	A small lump of rock orbiting around the Sun
Atom	The smallest part of an element.
Atomic energy	Another word for nuclear energy.
Attract	Two things pulling towards each other.
Auditory nerve (*ord-i-tory*)	A nerve that carries electrical signals (impulses) from the ear to the brain.
Axis (*acks-iss*)	Imaginary vertical line that goes from one pole of the Earth to the other. The Earth spins around on this line.
Bacterium	A type of microbe (bigger than a virus). (Plural = bacteria.)
Balanced diet	Eating a wide variety of foods to give us all the things that we need.
Balanced forces	When two forces are the same strength, but working in opposite directions.
Ball and socket joint	Flexible joint where the bones can move freely in all directions. eg hip joint.
Bar magnet	A straight magnet, shaped like a small bar.
Basalt (*ba-salt*)	An igneous rock with very tiny crystals.
Base	A chemical which reacts with an acid to form a salt.
Bauxite (*borcks-ite*)	Aluminium ore.
Biceps (*bye-seps*)	Muscle found at the front of the arm between the shoulder and elbow.
Bimetallic strip (*bye-met-al-lick*)	A strip of two different metals stuck together, that bends when it gets hot.
Biomass (*bye-O-mass*)	Any fuel that comes from plants, animals, or their wastes, eg wood, methane from rotting plants, etc.
Bird	Vertebrate with feathers, eg an eagle.
Black	A surface which absorbs all colours.
Blood	Made out of cells and a liquid called plasma. It flows around the body carrying various substances which are either made by the body or needed by the body.
Blood vessel	Tubes in which blood flows. There are capillaries, veins and arteries.
Boiling point	When a liquid is at its boiling point it is as hot as it can get. It is evaporating as fast as it can.
Bonds	Forces holding particles together.
Bone	Hard substance containing calcium that is used to make the skeleton in vertebrates.
Bone marrow	Found in the middle of some bones. It makes red blood cells.
Brain	Organ that controls what the body does.
Breathing (*bree-thing*)	Moving muscles to change the shape of your lungs to get air in and out.
Breathing rate	The number of times you breathe in a minute.
Breathing system	Set of organs that allows air to be taken into and out of the body (lungs, windpipe, diaphragm).

Brine	A solution of common salt and water.
Bronchitis (bron-**kite**-iss)	When the lining of the tubes leading to the lungs becomes swollen and sore.
Budding	The way yeast cells divide. A small cell (bud) grows from another cell.
Burning	When a chemical combines with oxygen, giving a chemical reaction and releasing light and heat energy.
Cable grip	Part of a plug that holds the cable, and stops the wires being pulled out of the pins.
Caffeine	A stimulant that increases the speed that nerves carry impulses. Is found in coffee, tea and cola drinks.
Camera	A box that lets light through a hole in one side, to form an image.
Cancer	Disease when some cells grow very fast. Can cause death.
Capillaries (cap-**pill**-arr-ees)	The smallest blood vessels. Substances enter and leave the blood through the thin walls of capillaries.
Carbohydrate (car-bO-**high**-drate)	Substance found in food that is used for energy.
Carbon dioxide	A gas which will turn limewater milky.
Carnivore	An animal that only eats other animals.
Carpel (car-pull)	Female reproductive organ found in flowers, and is made of a stigma, style and ovary.
Cartilage (cart-ill-lidge)	Slippery substance that covers the ends of bones in joints to stop them wearing away. Ears and the nose are also made from this.
Catalytic converter	A metal catalyst fitted to a car exhaust which helps to reduce pollution.
Cell (biology) (sell)	The basic unit which living things are made of. The smallest part of an organism.
Cell (physics) (sell)	It contains a store of chemical energy that can produce electricity. The scientific name for a battery.
Cell membrane (sell mem-brain)	Controls what goes into and out of a cell.
Cell wall	Tough wall around plant cells. Helps to support the cell.
Centipede (sent-ip-eed)	Type of arthropod with long thin body divided into sections, with many pairs of legs.
Cervix (sir-vicks)	Ring of muscle at the bottom of the uterus in females.
Chalk	Soft white or grey rock formed from the shells of small sea animals.
Chemical energy	The kind of energy stored in chemicals. Food, fuels and cells (batteries) all contain chemical energy.
Chemical formula	A combination of symbols and numbers that show how many atoms of different kinds there are in a particular compound.
Chemical reaction	A type of change when chemical substances are changed into new chemical substances, eg respiration.
Chemically weathered	Rock that is broken down through chemical reactions.
Chlorophyll (klor-O-fill)	Green substance found inside chloroplasts.
Chloroplast (klor-O-plast)	Green disc containing chlorophyll. Found in plant cells. Where the plant makes food using photosynthesis.
Choice chamber	Piece of equipment that allows scientists to test how environmental factors affect small animals.
Chromatography (krow-mat-og-graph-ee)	Separating dissolved solids from one another. The solids are usually coloured.
Chromosome (crow-mow-sOme)	Thread-like strands in the nucleus of a cell. They contain the instructions for a living thing.
Cilia (sill-ee-a)	Small hairs growing from some cells that can sweep things along.
Ciliated epithelial cell (sil-lee-ay-ted epp-ith-eel-lee-al)	A cell that lines an organ and has cilia.
Circuit (sir-kit)	A complete loop that electricity flows around.
Circulatory system (serk-you-late-or-ee)	Carries oxygen and food around the body. Contains the heart and blood vessels.
Circumcision (sir-cum-siz-shun)	Removal of the foreskin.
Classification (clas-if-ik-ay-shun)	Placing things into groups according to what they look like.
Clockwise moment	The turning effect of a force in a clockwise direction around a pivot.
Clot	When blood becomes solid.
Coal	A fossil fuel made from the remains of plants.
Cobalt	A metal that is a magnetic material.
Cocaine	Very powerful and harmful stimulant that causes blocked arteries and mental problems.
Cochlea (cok-lee-a)	The part of the ear that changes vibrations into electrical impulses.
Cold blooded	Animal with a body temperature that changes with the surroundings.
Combination reaction	When chemicals combine to form a new substance.
Combustion	The scientific word for burning.
Common salt	A chemical we use to make things taste 'salty'.
Community (com-mew-nit-ee)	All the plants and animals that live in a habitat.
Compass	A magnetised piece of metal that can swing around. It points north.
Competition (com-pet-tish-un)	Organisms try to get things they need before other organisms get them. Organisms are said to 'compete' with each other.
Component (com-pO-nent)	Something in a circuit, like a bulb, switch or motor.
Compound	A substance made of more than one element chemically joined together.
Compressed	Squeezed together.
Concave lens	A lens which is thinner in the middle and causes the rays of light to spread out.
Concentrate	We concentrate a solution by adding more of the solute to it.
Condenser	A piece of apparatus that cools down gases to turn them into liquids.
Condensing	A gas turning into a liquid.
Conduction (con-duck-shun)	The way heat travels through solids.
Conductor (con-duck-ter)	A material that lets energy travel through it easily.
Cone	Something used to contain the seeds of conifers.
Conifer (con-if-er)	A plant with needle-shaped leaves. Reproduces using seeds found in cones.
Conservation of Mass	The idea that the total mass of all the reactants in a chemical reaction is the same as the total mass of all the products.
Constellation (con-stell-ay-shun)	A pattern of stars.
Constipation (con-stip-ay-shun)	When the intestines get blocked up.
Consumer	An organism that has to eat other organisms to stay alive. Animals are consumers.
Contact force	A force that needs to touch an object before it can affect it, eg friction.
Continuous variation	The differences in one feature change gradually and have a whole range of values, eg human heights.
Contracting	Getting smaller.
Contractions (con-track-shuns)	The uterus starts to push out the baby during labour.
Convection (con-veck-shun)	A way that heat travels through liquids and gases.
Convection current (con-veck-shun)	A flow of liquid or gas caused by part of it being heated or cooled more than the rest.
Converge (con-verj)	Come together.

Converging lens (con-**verj**-ing)	Another name for a convex lens.
Convex lens	A lens which is fatter in the middle and causes the rays of light to come together.
Cord (biology)	Carries food, oxygen and waste between the placenta and the growing fetus.
Core	A solid bar inside an electromagnet. Usually made of iron.
Corrode (cor-**road**)	When something (such as stone or metal) reacts with chemicals in the air or water and gets worn away.
Corrosion (cor-**row**-shun)	When something (such as stone or metal) reacts with chemicals in the air or water and is worn away or changed into a different compound.
Corrosive (cor-**row**-sive)	Substances that attack metals, stonework and skin are called corrosive.
Coverslip	Thin piece of glass used to hold a specimen in place on a slide.
Crust	The solid rocks at the surface of the Earth.
Crustacean (crust-**ay**-shun)	Type of arthropod with a chalky shell and 5–7 pairs of legs, eg a lobster.
Crystals (**kris**-tals)	Pieces of a mineral with sharp edges.
Current	A flow of electricity.
Cyan (**sye**-an)	Secondary colour made by mixing green and blue light (greeny-blue).
Cytoplasm (**site**-O-plaz-m)	Jelly inside a cell where the cell's activities happen.
Daily changes	Changes in the physical factors of an environment which happen during a day. eg it gets dark at night.
Day	24 hours. The time it takes the Earth to spin once on its axis.
Decibel (dB) (**dess**-i-bell)	Unit for measuring the loudness of a sound.
Deciduous tree (dess-**idd**-you-us)	A tree that drops its leaves in winter, eg oak tree.
Decomposers	Microbes and other smaller organisms, which break down dead plants and animals and waste. eg bacteria and fungi.
Decompose	To break down into smaller pieces.
Deforestation (dee-for-es-**stay**-shun)	Removing trees from an area.
Degrees Celsius (°C)	The units for measuring temperature.
Density	The amount of mass that 1 cm^3 of a substance has. Measured in g/cm^3.
Deposition	When moving water drops rock fragments or grains.
Depressant	Drug that decreases the speed at which nerves carry impulses, eg alcohol.
Diagnosis (dye-ag-**nO**-sis)	To tell someone the name of their disease or condition.
Diaphragm (**dye**-a-fram)	Sheet of muscle underneath the lungs. It helps to work the lungs.
Diet	The food that you eat.
Diffusion (dif-you-**shun**)	The natural movement of particles from a place where there are a lot of them to a place where there are fewer of them.
Digestion (dye-**jes**-jun)	Process that breaks food into soluble substances in our bodies.
Digestive juice	A liquid containing enzymes that break down food.
Digestive system (dye-**jest**-iv)	The group of organs that carries out digestion.
Dilute	We dilute a solution by adding more of the solvent to it.
Discontinuous variation	The differences in one feature have only a few options, eg human eye colours.
Disease	When some processes that normally happen in the body do not happen in the way that they should.
Displacement	When one element takes the place of another.

Dissolving (dizz-**olv**-ing)	When a solid splits up and mixes with a liquid to make a solution.
Distillation (diss-till-**ay**-shun)	The process of separating a liquid from a solution by evaporating the liquid and then condensing it.
Distribution (diss-trib-**you**-shun)	The places where an organism can be found in a habitat.
Diverge (die-**verj**)	Spread out.
Diverging lens (die-**verj**-ing)	Another name for a concave lens.
Drag	Air resistance and water resistance are both sometimes called drag.
Drug	Substance that affects the way your body works.
Ear bones	Small bones which transmit the vibrations of the eardrum to the inner ear.
Eardrum	A thin membrane inside the ear which vibrates when sound reaches it.
Earth	The planet we live on.
Earth wire	The green and yellow wire in a cable or plug.
Echinoderm (ek-**eye**-no-derm)	Invertebrate with a body in five parts, eg a starfish.
Echo (**eck**-O)	A sound which is reflected back from something solid.
Ecstasy	A stimulant that can cause depression, mental illness and even death.
Effort	The force put on something.
Egestion (ee-**jes**-jun)	When faeces are pushed out of the anus.
Egg cell	The female sex cell (female gamete).
Ejaculation (edge-ack-you-**lay**-shun)	Semen is pumped out of a man's penis into the top of the vagina during sexual intercourse.
Elastic	Any substance that will return to its original shape and size after it has been stretched or squashed.
Electric current	The flow of electrons around a circuit.
Electrical energy	The kind of energy carried by electricity.
Electrical insulator	Something which does not allow electricity through it easily.
Electricity	A common word for 'electrical current'.
Electrodes (ell-**eck**-troads)	Rods used in electrolysis.
Electrolysis (ell-eck-**troll**-le-sis)	Splitting up a chemical using electricity.
Electromagnet	A coil of wire with electricity flowing in it. An electromagnet has a magnetic field like a bar magnet.
Electron	Tiny particle that flows around a circuit.
Element	All the atoms in an element are the same. A substance that cannot be split up into anything simpler by chemical reactions.
Elliptical (el-**lip**-tick-al)	Oval shaped. The shape of a planet's orbit around the Sun.
Embryo (animal) (**em**-bree-O)	Tiny new human life which grows in the uterus.
Embryo (plant) (**em**-bree-O)	Tiny plant, found inside a seed, with a very small shoot and a very small root.
Emit (em-**mit**)	To give out energy.
Endothermic	A chemical reaction that takes in heat from its surroundings.
Energy	Something that is needed to make things happen.
Energy flow diagram	A diagram to show energy changes.
Engulf	When a white blood cell completely surrounds a microbe and destroys it.
Environment	The surroundings of an organism, made up of physical factors and living factors.
Environmental factors	Things in an environment that can change something about an organism.

Environmental variation	Differences between organisms caused by environmental factors.
Enzyme	A chemical that can speed up a chemical reaction such as breaking up large molecules.
Epithelial (*epp-ith-eel-lee-al*)	Cell with cilia found in the lungs
Erection	When the penis becomes stiff.
Erosion	The movement of loose and weathered rock.
Estimate	An 'estimate' of something is a rough idea of how big something is or how many there are. To 'estimate' something means to work out an estimate.
Ethanol	The alcohol found in some drinks.
Ethene	A small molecule made of carbon and hydrogen.
Evaporation (*ev-app-or-ay-shun*)	A liquid turning into a gas.
Evergreen tree	Trees that keep their leaves in winter, eg pine tree.
Evidence	Information that helps to prove that an idea is correct.
Evolution (*eve-ol-oo-shun*)	When survival of the fittest happens over and over again and changes the features of animals and plants over thousands of years.
Excretion (*ex-cree-shun*)	Getting rid of waste substances that have been made in the body by chemical reactions, eg carbon dioxide from respiration.
Excretory system (*ex-cree-tor-ee*)	Gets rid of waste from our bodies.
Exhale	To breathe out.
Exoskeleton (*ex-O-skel-e-ton*)	Thick outer covering found on arthropods.
Exothermic	A reaction that releases heat into the surroundings.
Expand	To get bigger.
Eyepiece lens	The part of the microscope you look down.
Faeces (*fee-sees*)	Waste food material produced by the intestines.
Fallopian tube	Carries egg cells from the ovaries to the uterus. Fertilisation happens here.
Fat	Substance found in food that is stored to be used for energy in the future. It also helps to keep heat in our bodies.
Fatty acid	Fats are digested to form fatty acids.
Fermentation	The type of anaerobic respiration carried out by yeast. It produces carbon dioxide and ethanol.
Fern	A plant that has many small waterproof leaves. Reproduces using spores.
Fertilisation (*fert-ill-eyes-ay-shun*)	Joining of a male sex cell (gamete) with a female sex cell (gamete).
Fetus (*fee-tus*)	After an embryo has grown all its organs it is called a fetus. This is usually at about 10 weeks.
Fibre (*fy-ber*)	Substance found in food which cannot be used by the body. It helps to keep our intestines clean.
Filament (biology)	Part of the stamen. It supports the anther.
Filament (physics)	The thin coil of metal wire inside a light bulb that glows when electricity is flowing.
Filter (light)	Something which only lets certain colours through and absorbs the rest.
Filtering (chemistry)	Separating things that have not dissolved, from a liquid. The liquid is passed through a filter to do this.
Fire triangle	A triangle that shows the three things a fire must have to keep burning: fuel, oxygen and heat.
Fish	Vertebrate with wet scales, fins and gills, eg a salmon.
Fixed compositon	The numbers of atoms of different elements in a particular compound is always the same.
Fixed joint	Where bones meet but cannot move, eg joints in the skull.
Flexible joint	Where bones meet and can be moved by muscles.

Flower	Plant organ containing smaller reproductive organs – carpel (female) and stamen (male).
Flowering plant	A plant with large, flat leaves. Reproduces using seeds found in fruits. Fruits and seeds form from flowers.
Fluid	A gas or a liquid.
Focusing wheel	Part of a microscope that you turn to allow you to see the image clearly.
Food	The substances we eat to give us energy and nutrients.
Food chain	A way of showing what eats what in a habitat.
Food web	Many food chains linked together.
Force	A push or a pull.
Force meter	A piece of equipment, containing a spring, used to measure forces.
Force multiplier	Something that turns a small force into a larger force, eg a lever.
Foreskin	A covering of skin protecting the head of the penis.
Fossil	The remains of a dead animal or plant that became trapped in layers of sediment and turned into rock.
Fossil fuels	Fuels that were formed from the remains of dead plants and animals, eg coal, oil, natural gas.
Fractionating tower (*frac-shon-ay-ting*)	Large tower used to separate the different liquids in crude oil.
Freeze-thaw	A kind of weathering that happens when water gets into a crack and freezes. The freezing water expands and makes the crack bigger.
Freezing point	The temperature at which a liquid turns into a solid.
Frequency (*free-kwen-see*)	The number of waves each second.
Friction	A force that tries to slow things down when two things rub against each other.
Fruit	Something used to carry the seeds of a flowering plant. Can be fleshy or dry.
Fuel	A chemical which can release heat energy when it reacts.
Fulcrum	A point around which something turns. Another name for a pivot.
Full Moon	The phase of the Moon when it looks like a bright, full circle.
Function	Something's job.
Fungi	Organisms that secrete enzymes and absorb the digested products. They cannot photosynthesise.
Fuse	A piece of wire that melts if too much electricity flows through it.
Galaxy	Millions of stars grouped together.
Gamete (*gam-meet*)	Scientific word for sex cell.
Gas	Something made of particles that are very spread out and have no bonds between them.
Gas exchange	Taking oxygen into the blood and getting rid of carbon dioxide into the lungs. Happens in the air sacs in the lungs.
Generate	Make electricity by turning a magnet inside coils of wire.
Generator	Large coil of wire with a magnet inside. When the magnet is turned, electricity is produced in the coil of wire.
Genes	Small pieces of DNA that each control a particular characteristic.
Genetic variation (*jen-et-tick*)	Another name for inherited variation.
Geothermal power (*jee-O-therm-al*)	Making electricity using heat from hot rocks underground.
Germination (*jerm-in-ay-shun*)	When a seed first starts to grow.
Glands	The glands in the male reproductive system add a special liquid to the sperm cells to make semen. There are other sorts of glands in the body which secrete hormones.

The Periodic Table

Key:
atomic number ——
name of element ——

30	**Zn**	atomic symbol
zinc		
65		mass number

Legend boxes: **metal** | **semi metal** | **non metal**

1	**H**
hydrogen	
1	

Main Table

1	2											13	14	15	16	17	18
																	2 **He** helium 4
3 **Li** lithium 7	4 **Be** beryllium 9											5 **B** boron 11	6 **C** carbon 12	7 **N** nitrogen 14	8 **O** oxygen 16	9 **F** fluorine 19	10 **Ne** neon 20
11 **Na** sodium 23	12 **Mg** magnesium 24											13 **Al** aluminium 27	14 **Si** silicon 28	15 **P** phosphorus 31	16 **S** sulphur 32	17 **Cl** chlorine 35	18 **Ar** argon 40
19 **K** potassium 40	20 **Ca** calcium 40	21 **Sc** scandium 45	22 **Ti** titanium 48	23 **V** vanadium 51	24 **Cr** chromium 52	25 **Mn** manganese 55	26 **Fe** iron 56	27 **Co** cobalt 59	28 **Ni** nickel 59	29 **Cu** copper 64	30 **Zn** zinc 65	31 **Ga** gallium 70	32 **Ge** germanium 73	33 **As** arsenic 75	34 **Se** selenium 79	35 **Br** bromine 80	36 **Kr** krypton 84
37 **Rb** rubidium 85	38 **Sr** strontium 88	39 **Y** yttrium 89	40 **Zr** zirconium 91	41 **Nb** niobium 93	42 **Mo** molybdenum 96	43 **Tc** technetium 98	44 **Ru** ruthenium 101	45 **Rh** rhodium 103	46 **Pd** palladium 106	47 **Ag** silver 108	48 **Cd** cadmium 112	49 **In** indium 115	50 **Sn** tin 119	51 **Sb** antimony 122	52 **Te** tellurium 128	53 **I** iodine 127	54 **Xe** xenon 131
55 **Cs** caesium 133	56 **Ba** barium 137	57 **La** lanthanum 139	72 **Hf** hafnium 178	73 **Ta** tantalum 181	74 **W** tungsten 184	75 **Re** rhenium 186	76 **Os** osmium 190	77 **Ir** iridium 192	78 **Pt** platinum 195	79 **Au** gold 197	80 **Hg** mercury 201	81 **Tl** thallium 204	82 **Pb** lead 207	83 **Bi** bismuth 209	84 **Po** polonium 209	85 **At** astatine 210	86 **Rn** radon 222
87 **Fr** francium 223	88 **Ra** radium 226	89 **Ac** actinium 227	104 **Rf** rutherfordium 261	105 **Db** dubnium 262	106 **Sg** Seaborgium 263	107 **Bh** bohrium 264	108 **Hs** hassium 265	109 **Mt** meitnerium 268	110 **Uun** Ununnilium 269	111 **Uuu** Unununium 272	112 **Uub** Ununbium 269		114 **Uuq** ununquadium ?		116 **Uuh** Ununhexium ?		118 **Uuo** Ununoctium ?

gaps left for undiscovered elements

Lanthanides

58 **Ce** cerium 140	59 **Pr** praseodymium 141	60 **Nd** neodymium 144	61 **Pm** promethium 145	62 **Sm** samarium 150	63 **Eu** europium 152	64 **Gd** gadolinium 157	65 **Tb** terbium 159	66 **Dy** dysprosium 163	67 **Ho** holmium 165	68 **Er** erbium 167	69 **Tm** thulium 169	70 **Yb** ytterbium 173	71 **Lu** lutetium 175

Actinides

90 **Th** thorium 232	91 **Pa** protactinium 231	92 **U** uranium 238	93 **Np** neptunium 237	94 **Pu** plutonium 244	95 **Am** americium 243	96 **Cm** curium 247	97 **Bk** berkelium 247	98 **Cf** californium 251	99 **Es** einsteinium 252	100 **Fm** fermium 257	101 **Md** mendelevium 258	102 **No** nobelium 259	103 **Lr** lawrencium 262

Index